THE
SURGEON PROBATIONERS

THE
SURGEON PROBATIONERS

R S Allison

Blackstaff Press

Published by Blackstaff Press Limited, 255A Upper Newtownards Road, Belfast BT4 3JF, with the assistance of the Eastern Health and Social Services Board. The publishers wish to thank the staff of Royal Victoria Hospital who helped in the preparation of this book and in particular the late Dr. Allison's secretary.

ISBN 0 85640 145 5

Printed in Northern Ireland by Graphic Printing Services.

Contents

List of illustrations   vii
Foreword   xi
Introduction   xvii

Part 1
Appointment of Surgeon Probationers   1
The Outbreak of War and First Entries;   11
    Surgeon Rear Admiral R. J. Willan, R.N.V.R.
Contribution of the Belfast Medical School   15
The Surgeon Probationers in Action   28
Some Reminiscences of the R.N. Hospital, Haslar in 1918   38
Personal Recollections of Experiences in the Mediterranean   47
    in the Closing Phase of the War
Envoy   58
Part 2
The Clinical Notes by R. J. Willan   62
Index to *The Clinical Notes*   115

Appendix A   118
Appendix B   119
Index to *The Surgeon Probationers*   140

List of Illustrations

Fig. 1 Transcript of Warrant for Surgeon's Mates, circa 1711   3

Fig. 2 Relative Strength of Medical Officers in Army and Navy
in 1914   4

Victor Millington Synge, Surgeon Probationer   16

Frederick Martin Brice Allen, M.D., F.R.C.P. (Lond.)   17

George Dixon Fisher McFadden, M.Ch., F.R.C.S. Eng.   18

Title page from R. J. Willan's handbook   62

To the memory of a gifted teacher:
Staff Surgeon R.J. Willan, R.N.V.R.
for his 'Clinical Notes'.

Foreword

It is a particular pleasure to be afforded the opportunity of contributing a foreword to Dr. Allison's book on the Surgeon Probationers of the First World War, for it provides an appropriate and timely sequel to his classic work on Sea Diseases which brought us to the end of the nineteenth century.

Apart from several admirable contributions to more enlightened casualty management by Surgeons of the Fleet and descriptions of revolutionary surgical techniques practised by young temporary surgeon lieutenants in naval hospitals, we are less well informed about the medical aspects of World War One than World War Two. Dr. Allison has now made good that gap through the experiences of the young students who responded so magnificently to the challenge of medical responsibility in the uncomfortable, wet and hazardous environment of those small ships which played so vital a role in keeping our sea lanes open.

Fortunately for the surgeon probationers, thrust into a bewildering situation for which they were quite unprepared, they found a champion in the person of Staff Surgeon R. J. Willan who understood young men and had a special facility for subjecting the complexities of the most puzzling diagnostic problem to objective systematic analysis which, through lack of experience, the surgeon probationer was unable to do himself. These 'Guide Posts', as Willan called them, subsequently came to be incorporated into the 'Hat Pegs' of his clinical teaching at the Royal Victoria Infirmary, Newcastle, where he succeeded Grey Turner as Professor of Surgery, when I myself was a student there. Like Sydenham before him, Willan brought down the aspiring specialist from the rarefied realm of theoretical conjecture to the harsh realities of a bedside situation demanding responsibile decision.

The inclusion of Willan's handbook places me under a two-fold obligation: to Willan, a superb teacher who unconsciously placed my faltering steps on the road both to the Navy and a career in surgery and to Dr. Allison himself, whose exemplary support and distinguished contribution to naval medicine over the past sixty years have demonstrated the undeniable necessity for a strong, highly professional reserve of medical officers of the Royal Navy: in peace complementing, and in war, an integral part of an elite team of experts in modern maritime medicine. Although Dr. Allison reached the highest rank in the Royal Naval Volunteer Reserve and received the Volunteer Decoration, these acknowledgements barely recognise the extent of the contribution he has made. That contribution also bears testimony to the influence of his own medical school, Queen's University, Belfast, upon the Royal Navy. It may not be out of place to observe that Captain Cook, to whom Allison gives just credit for his remarkable success in preserving the health of seamen during three long voyages round the world, reserves his highest place for a Belfast man, James Patten. He was surgeon of the *Resolution* during the outstandingly successful second voyage. Forster, the naturalist, informs us that 'our worthy surgeon, Mr Patten, took the best precautions possible to preserve the health of all on board, by suggesting the proper methods to Captain Cook, and by watching over us with unremitting assiduity. I will venture to affirm, that it is to him alone under Providence, that many of us are indebted to our lives...' James Patten was born in Northern Ireland about 1748, the son of the Reverend William Patten, and joined *Resolution* on the 12th December 1771, leaving the Navy after the voyage to practise surgery and midwifery in Dublin. Some of his specimens are in the National Museum of Ireland.

It is obviously impossible to assess the influence of Willan's hand-book, but it must have had as great an impact upon the surgeon proba-tioners of the early twentieth century as those early predecessors, of equal practical merit, written for surgeons' mates of the sixteenth and seventeenth centuries by Wylliam Clowes and John Woodall. In giving it such prominence, Allison tacitly acknowledges its place in the exploits of the individuals recorded in later chapters. Much of it is as relevant today as it was sixty years ago, even though Wakeley, then only a surgeon lieutenant, had the tenacity to challenge — rightly as it trans-pired — Willan's support for the use of picric acid, the topical application then in vogue for the first-aid treatment of burns. Clinical freedom and the right to challenge traditional practices, whatever the rank of their protagonists, remains the jealously-guarded prerogative of the young naval surgeon today. No doubt, the discipline of maintaining the 400-year-old tradition of daily examination of the sick and keeping a journal have taught him to think for himself, with results now demonstrated in the high standards of professional practice and of scientific contributions to current medical literature.

There is nevertheless a disturbing parallel between the pre-1914 philosophy and that which is prevalent today, for a shortfall in medical manpower in times of national emergency is the inevitable sequel. In 1914, it forced the Medical Department to look for medical students to man the ships, belatedly recognised to be in need of doctors, and caused the Medical Director General himself to make his historic appeal for volunteers in Edinburgh. The full report of that speech, which placed proper emphasis upon preventive medicine, does not however bear close scrutiny and his spirited defence of the Medical Service ignored the glaring disparity then existing between the Army and the Navy in terms of conditions of service, opportunities for specialisation and advancement, which the Dean of Medicine, Sir William Turner, was not slow to point out. Later, the British Medical Association, powerfully representing the exasperation of its naval members, detailed, to the embarrassment of the Navy, the disadvantaged position of the naval medical officer. Those anomalies certainly no longer exist, but the battleship mentality to which Allison refers had its origin in rigid executive attitudes which gave priority to ship building but failed significantly to take into adequate account the needs and welfare of the men, an error Nelson never committed!

In times of economic depression, it is as tempting as in the pre-1914 era, to preserve costly and complicated hardware at the expense of trained and experienced hands who provide the essential expertise, which no longer can be recruited from raw untrained volunteers responding loyally to a national emergency. Today's sophisticated ships require a broad spectrum of medical specialisation to provide the preventive, scientific and clinical skills required to support naval operations. But it must be remembered by those who take such skills for granted that it now takes eight years to train a doctor and some thirteen years or more before he has mastered his speciality; while the academic qualifications of today's medical technician, medical assistant and naval nurse merely provide the starting point for a long period of training. When Sir Gilbert Blane arrived on the West Indies Station in 1780, he was quick to note the care taken to conserve stores and armaments, but observed that 'it is on the numbers and vigour of hands that success must depend in the conflict with the elements and in the hour of battle ... money has metaphorically been called the sinews of war; but the most indispensable article for the efficient purpose of war is the sinews literally and properly so called, belonging to the living engines by whose energies it is carried on.'

For that reason, Dr. Allison's proposal that the number of medical students attached to RNR Divisions should be increased, in order to allow them to spend three to six months of their secondment in small ships at sea, has obvious merit, for it would ensure an adequate pool of medical manpower which could be called upon in time of crisis. Unfortunately however, the vast amount of equipment packed into a modern warship increasingly encroaches upon living accommodation, creating the problem of providing enough sea experience even for surgeon lieutenants under training. Reliance must therefore be placed upon a strong medical naval reserve providing diverse skills and teaching abilities if the Naval Medical Service is to offer the considerable range of expertise the Service demands.

The book's concluding chapters, written in a light and anecdotal vein, admirably capture the spirit of the age, with good humour, comradeship and Service loyalties triumphing over the contrasting experiences of hardship, high seas, boredom, sudden danger and sharp, bloody actions. At Jutland, the destructive potential of high explosive shells was terrifyingly demonstrated as steel splinters, broken oil and steam pipes, cordite fires in gun turrets and devastating explosions claimed men and ships and established new patterns of injury with illunderstood complications. The traditional one to three ratio of killed to injured in battle was converted to an appalling nine to one! The surgeon probationers evidently acquitted themselves well. At least five gained the DSC and there are fascinating insights into hitherto unpublished stories of courage, initiative and innovation, although Abercrombie's quick-witted quip concerning the pulmonary complications of casualties following the attack on Zeebrugge rather too obviously disclosed the lamentable lack of knowledge which still prevails about the effects of high explosives in closed environments. This is likely to be the major problem in future conflicts and one which should attract far more research resources than it currently receives.

One is apt to forget how easily an epidemic can immobilise a ship or a Fleet and time has blurred the impact of the world-wide influenza epidemic of 1918 which fell with devastating suddenness and totality upon the ship in which the author was serving in the Eastern Mediterranean. Within thirty-six hours only seven officers and men were capable of duty. Even in the Second World War, no less than 150 men out of a complement of 620 in a light cruiser in which I was serving in the early years of the war went down with malaria causing great problems in ship management.

Epidemic diseases have been largely overcome in time of peace and effective preventive measures may suffice in time of war, but new environmental hazards have taken their place and can only be understood by adequate training in maritime medicine which no scheme for the emergency mobilisation of medical manpower will provide in any future war. This, I believe, is the message Surgeon Captain R. S. Allison RNVR is endeavouring to convey. If it has any other, it is that the Navy is fun!

Surgeon Vice-Admiral Sir James Watt.

Introduction

After the lapse of over sixty years it is difficult to collect information about the surgeon probationers — those young medical students who were permitted to interrupt their studies during the First World War between 1914-18 and who volunteered to serve for a time in the Royal Navy. They came from medical schools in England, Scotland, Ireland, Wales, and some of the Dominion universities. Their calling-up for service was approved by the General Medical Council and the Medical Department of the Royal Navy. The reasons for their enrolment temporarily in the Navy were because of the outbreak of war, the acute shortage of regular serving medical officers, and the need to provide some medical cover for the crews of small ships, such as destroyers or sloops, for which qualified doctors could not then be spared. There was a progressive increase in the number of such small ships after the outbreak of war, and neither destroyers nor sloops carried a sick berth attendant. The individual surgeon probationer who volunteered found himself in charge of the day-to-day care of the crews of these ships, although being in a position to call upon for help a fully qualified naval surgeon in an emergency.

Their employment bore some resemblance to that of their forebears, the eighteenth century 'surgeon's mates', who were even less qualified and who did not hold commissioned rank. This privilege, with their single gold stripe, set the surgeon probationers in a much stronger position to play the role of doctor, and in fact it was under this title by which they were familiarly known to the officers and men of the ships which they served. Surgeon probationers were required to provide evidence of good character and to have advanced so far in their education at an established medical school as to have passed the second medical examination in anatomy and physiology. Early in the war many of those who volunteered were already in their third or fourth year of study and, having served for a short time as a student, re-entered the navy as fully qualified surgeons after returning to their medical school and graduating.

Some thirty students came from the Belfast Medical School and Royal

Victoria Hospital alone, and altogether the total number from all sources during the four years of war of surgeon probationers amounted to well over one thousand. The students were entered into the R.N.V.R. and at first given the rank of 'surgeon probationer' but during the last year of the war, with the regrading of medical officers in general to bring them into line with the executive branch, they were promoted to sub-lieutenant or surgeon sub-lieutenant in preference to the old, rather equivocal title surgeon probationer. The failure to reintroduce them in subsequent wars merely reflected altered circumstances of the times because there was no shortage of doctors then and it was decided that it was better for students to allow them to continue their studies un-interrupted until they became fully qualified before allowing them to enter the services. In 1914 the surgeon probationers, however, supplied a vital need and in retrospect it does not appear that the interruption of their studies made any material difference to their subsequent careers. On the contrary, the experience seems to have been of benefit.

I am grateful to Miss V. Riley of the Admiralty Historical Library, Ministry of Defence, Empress State Building, London for her assistance in uncovering details of many of the surgeon probationers. To the Medical Director-General, Surgeon Vice-Admiral J. Watt, I am indebted for his interest and valuable suggestions he made about the state of the Medical Department in 1914. To the Editor of the Journal of the Royal Naval Medical Service in which these articles appeared serially during 1976 I am grateful for permission to reproduce Surgeon Rear Admiral Willan's original little handbook entitled 'Clinical Notes for Surgeon Probationers'. My thanks are also due to the Eastern Health and Social Services Board whose Officers have been of very great assistance to me, and my special thanks are due to Mrs O. Russell of the office of Archives in the Royal Victoria Hospital who was responsible for typing the draft.

R. S. Allison

Part I

Appointment of Surgeon Probationers

In 1914 at the outbreak of war with Germany the Royal Navy was at the very zenith of its power. It had the largest battle fleet in the world, the most sophisticated weapons and a personnel superbly trained and disciplined to withstand the rigours which it was shortly to have placed upon it. If a certain complacency of attitude permeated the Admiralty and Parliament regarding it, this was excusable because of its long undenied ascendancy since Trafalgar as the world's greatest sea power. Even in the years before the war its leaders, like the redoubtable Jacky Fisher, the First Sea Lord, and his companion in office, Mr. Winston Churchill, were insisting on the urgent need for further stepping-up in the building programme of dreadnoughts and destroyers to ensure that Britain had a superiority over all other navies in these types of ship especially. Thinking was largely concerned with the battleship. The aeroplane was still in the experimental stage, and the torpedo and submarine had yet to demonstrate their power.

No one could forecast the shape of coming events or appreciate sufficiently the great part that was to be played during the war by the submarine, torpedo, and mine. Almost everyone assumed that, as in the Russo-Japanese conflict of 1904, the Fleets of Germany and Britain would engage in prodigious gun battles and that Britain would emerge victorious. There was some surprise, therefore, when the war at sea was ushered in quietly without any major Fleet engagement. Except for the Battle of the Falkland Islands, the Dogger Bank action, and the Battle of Jutland, this was for the most part the pattern of the war at sea. The fighting was done by the small ships, i.e. the destroyers, sloops, minesweepers and light cruisers. These bore the brunt throughout the four years of hostilities, the battleships and battle-cruisers upon which such store had been laid being largely held in reserve. The morale of their crews remained high, despite the comparative isolation of the chief base at Scapa Flow in the Orkneys, although it must have been severely tested at times owing to the long periods of waiting and the lack of opportunity given to meet the German High Sea Fleet in action. The latter, however, with the British blockade sapping its vitals, was unable to withstand the strain and as a result mutiny broke out among their ships so that before the end of the war it had lost most of its former power.

At the commencement of the war there was one unsatisfactory aspect of the service at least which was giving the Admiralty some concern. This was the shortage of naval medical officers. Recruiting to the naval medical service was at a low ebb. Indeed, it had been so during the whole of the 19th century when it had been allowed to fall into official neglect. In the Napoleonic wars of the 18th century there had been no dearth of doctors coming forward to join the Fleet, one of the chief inducements to do so being the prospect of earning a worthwhile share in prize money which had accumulated as a result of the capture of enemy ships. These inducements undoubtedly stirred young doctors to come forward and to give their services to well-known commanders who were vigorous and active leaders. Leonard Gillespie, an Ulsterman, was such an example. After serving an apprenticeship to a doctor in Armagh, he passed the required examinations at the Royal College of Surgeons in Dublin at the age of seventeen for 'surgeon's mate' and ultimately rose in the service to become Physician to the Mediterranean Fleet under Admiral Lord Nelson, having accumulated a considerable fortune by the time of his retirement, partly through prize money and partly through having charge at one period in his career of a large number of invalids and French prisoners-of-war in Martinique.

Neither the surgeons nor the surgeon's mates held commissioned rank during the 18th century. They were graded as warrant officers and occupied a relatively inferior position in a ship. Many of them had only an elementary training in medicine. As Smollett[1] describes, their test of competency was based on a purely verbal examination and was much too superficial to bear any comparison with modern procedures. Having passed, a young man had usually no difficulty in wartime in finding a berth as a surgeon's mate in a frigate where he took his place on the orlop deck and where his chief duties consisted of assisting the surgeon, dressing wounds, administering clysters, and treating ulcers and sores. (Fig. 1).

Unfortunately, many of the descriptions that have survived of surgeon's mates suggest that they were a drunken, profligate body of men, only a few being conspicuous for their reliability and bravery in action. However the Admiralty must have felt that times had so changed since the 18th century, and the character of the youth of 1914 was so different that some possible good could come from the recruiting

2

By the Principal Officers and
Commissioners of Her Majesties Navy.

Whereas, by a Certificate from the Master or Governors of the Mistery
and Comonalty of Barbers and Chyrurgeons of Lond, bearing date the
We are informed of your Ability and Fitness to
serve as Chyrurgeon's Mate of any of Her Majesties Ships of the
Rate. These are therefore to Authorize and Require you, forthwith to
make your Repair on Board Her Majesties Ship   as
Chyrurgeon's Mate, and there to Officiate in all Things proper to the
Duty of your place as becometh you, during her present intended
Voyage, and to be Obedient unto such Commands as you shall from
time to time receive from your Captain, or other Superior Officer in his
absence: As also the Chyrurgeon of the said Ship for the time being. For
which this shall be your Warrant. Dates at the Navy-Office this
day of   17

To   hereby
Appointed Chyrurgeon's Mate of Her Majesties Ship.

Fig 1. Transcript of Warrant for Surgeon's Mates circa 1711.

3

Relative Strength of Medical Officers in Army and Navy in 1914.*

			Total Personnel	Establishment of Medical Officers
Army			240,000	982
(a)	The Fleet	147,900		
	Dockyards and Civil Employees	56,600	204,500	525

*Suppl. to the Brit. Med. Jnl., 11th July, 1914.
'Report on the Shortage of Medical Officers in the Royal Navy'.

Fig. 2

of medical students in wartime to supplement the then existing acute shortage of fully qualified doctors in the service.

In 1904 the navy had an establishment of 594 medical officers, all of them qualified doctors. In that year there were 12,000 officers and men in the Fleet. By 1915 this figure had been raised to 146,000. The proportion of serving medical officers, however, was lower than it was in any other great navy and it was apparent that sufficient inducement was not being offered to attract young doctors to enter the service and make it their career. (Fig. 2).

The Royal Army Medical Corps had begun before 1914 to attract medical students from the different hospitals and universities into its ranks. These student dressers were given the title of 'Probationer Lieutenant' and the decision to take them into the R.A.M.C. was communicated to the Admiralty in May, 1913. It evoked much interest in view of the difficulty the navy was finding in obtaining sufficient number of qualified medical officers. Sir Charles Chadwyck-Healey,[2] who had done much to strengthen the position of the R.N.V.R. since 1903, expressed the view that attracting young medical students into the navy to serve on equal terms with the R.A.M.C. was a sound idea. He said, 'I have no doubt that one of the causes of the lack of interest in the naval service is a want of knowledge among the students of its present efficient state.'

Meanwhile, the Medical Director, Surgeon-General Sir Arthur May, gave an address to the medical students of Edinburgh University, the Principal occupying the chair. In this he set out to tell the students of coming events. He admitted that there was probably a stronger pull among Scottish students to serve in the land rather than the sea service but he pointed out that Scotland was shortly to become 'the greatest resort of the navy'. He remembered a time when it used to be a rare thing to see a warship larger than a gunboat in the Firth of Forth. Now, the greatest naval ports were to be on the Forth and he wished to commend the navy to them and to persuade young men to join the naval medical service. There was a shortage of doctors then. One of the chief reasons was because the navy was being judged by the conditions under which it operated thirty-five years earlier. At that time the navy was not efficient. Its medical officers were not up to the mark. The standard of nursing was tenth-rate. Hospitals were fifty years behind the time, both in their equipment and organisation. He could assure them that these conditions had now absolutely altered. Today there was no finer body of medical men. The nurses were second to none and the organisation and equipment of hospitals as fine as any in the world. He could assure them that the service today was an absolutely efficient and living branch of medicine.

Sir Arthur May put much enthusiasm into his lecture, and in retrospect laid himself open to some criticism as he failed to recognise the part his own medical department was playing in causing the shortage of naval surgeons. There was, it appears, little attempt on the part of the Medical Department of the Navy to provide for the proper training of specialists in naval hospitals nor, indeed, for the career-planning of those doctors which the navy was able to attract to its ranks. However, in one respect Sir Arthur showed great prescience in forecasting that one of the chief roles which the navy would have to play in wartime was that of protection of our overseas shipping because otherwise the country could not be assured against starvation and of the delivery of a sufficiency of munitions in wartime and this was bound to cause an enormous increase of escort type of vessels. In drawing attention to this point before the war the Medical Director General was undoubtedly correct.

After the lecture, the Principal, Sir William Turner, and the Dean of the Medical Faculty in Edinburgh University pointed out that the supply of the right sort of doctor for the navy was contingent on the official promise of increased opportunities for good professional work and adequate pay. When these provisions were fulfilled the university authorities would be prepared to do for the navy what they were already doing for the army and to give freely of their best. They would not be satisfied merely to attain numerical parity of medical officers with any other great navy. The numbers must be adequate for peace and war, and it must be realised that the navy was no longer the pleasant and varied service it used to be when the country held large squadrons on all the seas of the globe.

The principal existing grievances of naval medical officers were brought to the notice of the British Medical Association and, although it was unlikely in 1914 that anything very definite could be done to remedy them, the *British Medical Journal* published some of the principal defects. These related to such points as in ships cabins were not always available for use by medical officers. This in their opinion was an absolutely essential requirement.

When proceeding on foreign service medical officers were not granted passages for their wives and children, either outward or homeward as was the case in the R.A.M.C. This should be corrected.

As regards seniority in the service medical officers were to be granted equal authority and rank with combatant officers and were required to sit on boards or court martials on members of their own branch. This rule should be rescinded.

Specialization in the navy was to be encouraged and paid for in line with the practice in the R.A.M.C.

Six weeks annual leave had hitherto been the rule. When serving in home waters naval surgeons should be given three months' annual leave. Abroad, leave might be more difficult to arrange and officers could find themselves working in hospitals, doing day duty on and off for as long as three years without any leave. Leave was to be granted as often as practical and if necessary should be made cumulative, once a sufficiency of medical officers had been attained.

The senior medical officer in a ship, shore establishment or hospital should preside at boards for the survey of invalids. That such a board, consisting of commissioned medical officers, should need additonal supervision by an executive officer, in the opinion of the British Medical Association, was an insult to the medical profession.

The discrepancy in age between the medical and non-medical or executive branches in the navy should be overcome by promoting surgeons to 'Staff Surgeon' on completion of six years' service and to 'Fleet Surgeon' on completion of twelve years' service.

There were too few higher posts in the naval medical service to attract doctors, many officers being put on half pay, merely serving as ornaments to the navy list. In the R.A.M.C. forty-two higher ranks received full pay as compared to only nineteen in the navy. To give more Fleet Surgeons a chance of promotion, with higher full and retired pay, more senior officers could be employed as principal medical officers in barracks, dockyards, hospitals, hospital ships, and large training establishments such as Shotley and Whale Island.

Finally, although the sick berth staff, as Surgeon-General Sir Arthur May had stated, was second to none in quality, it was second to others in quantity and pay, and the British Medical Association recommended that when reforms were brought in, this deserving arm of the service must not be forgotten.

As can be seen, the creation of surgeon probationers in 1914 was determined chiefly by shortage of medical officers in the navy and whilst steps were being taken to set right the grievances the Admiralty issued Orders in Council[3] on 19 December 1913 as follows:

'No. 56/C.W.   SURGEON PROBATIONER, R.N.V.R. — RANK ESTABLISHED.

'Whereas by the Naval Forces Act, 1903, it is enacted that the Admiralty shall have power to raise and maintain a force to be called the Royal Naval Volunteer Reserve, and that any Volunteer enrolled under this Act, when serving for training afloat, or called out for actual service, shall be deemed to be serving in Your Majesty's Naval or Marine Force within the meaning of the Naval and Marine Pay and Pensions Act, 1865.

'And whereas we deem it expedient, under the authority conferred on us by the said Naval Forces Act, 1903, to establish a rank of Royal Naval Volunteer Reserve Officer to be entitled Surgeon Probationer:

'We beg leave humbly to recommend that Your Majesty may be graciously pleased by Your Order in Council to sanction the establishment of this rank accordingly, with relative rank, pay, hospital allowance, and special allowance when called out for actual service as set forth in the accompanying Schedule.'

Thus, pending the solution to the problem of staffing the navy with doctors, the Medical Department of the Navy were not slow in putting together regulations for the commissioning of a number of medical students as surgeon probationers. In the statement of the First Lord of the Admiralty, explaining the Navy Estimates for 1914, there appeared the following announcement:

'*A new Branch of the Royal Naval Medical Reserve is being formed consisting of Medical Students who have completed a certain portion of their training but are not fully qualified medical practitoners. These officers will be styled Surgeon Probationers and it is hoped that they will prove later on a valuable addition to the reserves of Medical Officers.*'

This was a bold step on the part of the Admiralty but it had the full support of the medical profession. The Deans of the various medical schools in England, Scotland and Ireland did their best to encourage students to volunteer as surgeon probationers for the navy. In creating the rank they had a good precedent, taking a leaf out of the pages of the 18th century and bringing the service into line with the R.A.M.C. The surgeon probationers were fully accredited students of a recognised university or medical school and were required to be of good character and to have advanced in their studies so as to have passed the second medical examination in anatomy and physiology, this being the most junior level at which they could be entered. But at the beginning of the war and for the first two years, many were more senior and had already entered the hospital phase of their training, being already experienced in clinical dressing and first-aid to the wounded. Whilst serving in the R.N.V.R. they came under the direction of the Medical Department of the Admiralty. They wore naval uniform and a single gold stripe, having a plain band of scarlet cloth placed underneath it. In consequence, because of their volunteer association, the gold stripe was wavy or undulating in character, and the badge on the uniform cap, whilst carrying a crown and anchor, had the letters R.N.V. embroidered over the boss. Later in the war, in 1918, when like other members of the Medical Department in the Navy they were granted the full status of commissioned officer their uniform was altered to include the executive curl to the gold braid.

The Medical Director General expressly stated that they were not to be used as substitutes for fully qualified surgeons but to be employed principally in giving first aid on board ship, and in naval hospitals and hospital ships acting as clinical clerks and dressers. The most useful site for their employment, however, was found to be in destroyers, sloops, and small escort vessels as these came into service during the war. In such they were left in medical charge of their ships' company but they were always in a position to obtain the advice of a fully qualified Surgeon, R.N. when this was required.

All applications for appointment had to be made to the Admiralty and to be accompanied by certificates of good character, physical fitness, and proof that the student was a member of a recognised medical school and had advanced so far in his studies as to have passed the second professional examination. The surgeon probationers received the full pay and allowances of their rank as sub-lieutenants and a uniform allowance. In ships they were granted the ordinary ship's rations but had to pay a small sum for the maintenance of their mess in the ward-room. They were entitled to pensions and gratuities in respect to injuries received on the basis of the awards of a similar kind made to other naval officers of corresponding rank. As regards the duration of their service they were required to engage for a minimum of six months and their liability to service was restricted to five years. Later, these rules and regulations were amended as follows:

(a) Surgeon probationers are to be granted reasonable leave of absence to attend their final examinations (Admiralty Order of January 1st, 1915.)
(b) If the period of leave granted (which has been fixed at three weeks) is not sufficient, the request of a probationer to be demobilized in order to return to his studies is never to be refused.

Further, the President of the General Medical Council directed that 'in the present emergency it is desirable that the fifth-year students now on duty with the Fleet should without delay become qualified for commissioned service. Their places might be taken by less advanced students who have passed the second professional examination, and have received special instruction in "dressing" and in other "first-aid" methods of dealing with the wounded.' Many medical students were eager to leave their studies and do service in the war and there was a good response to the opportunity offered to take on six months' duty as surgeon probationers in the navy. This system of rotation thus enabled the more senior students to return to their medical school and qualify in time to rejoin the navy as doctors before the end of hostilities. For those who came in towards the close of the war, when they returned to their medical schools they either rejoined their original year and qualified, or fell back for a year and qualified in medicine in the succeeding one.

1. Author of *Roderick Random*.

2. Sir Charles Edward Chadwyck-Healey, called to Bar 1872, Bt. cr. 1919. K.C.B. 1909; C.B. 1905; dd. 5.10.1919. Commander (Hon.) R.N.V.R. Captain R.N.V.R. 1914. Chairman of the Admiralty Volunteer Committee 1903-14.

3. Orders in Council for the Regulation of the Naval Service. Vol. IX 11th February, 1913 to 21st December, 1917.

The Outbreak of War and First Entries; Surgeon Rear Admiral R. J. Willan, R.N.V.R.

The immediate result of this Admiralty announcement was satisfactory. In universities and schools in London, the provinces, Wales, Scotland and Ireland, medical students, encouraged by the Deans of their respective faculties, began to apply for temporary commissions. By the outbreak of war on 4th August 1914 nearly forty names had been enrolled and were published in the Navy List. The first surgeon probationer so listed was Eric Lander Caldwell Smith, whose date of seniority was 22nd April, 1914. Others who had been commissioned before the outbreak of war were Alfred Henry Price (26th June); Edmund Keane (26th June); Alfred G. McColl (20th July); John Prestcott Johnson, William Tudor Evans, and William Griffiths (29th July). From this modest beginning during the four years of war the number grew steadily so that after four years and the conclusion of hostilities the number of volunteers commissioned as surgeon probationers was twelve hundred, this estimate being more of an understatement than the reverse. None of these young men had had any previous connection with the service and were all appointed to the Royal Naval Volunteer Reserve. Pending their individual appointment to ships they were listed or attached to base hospital ships such as H.M.H.S. *Plassy, Soudan, Rohilla*. All engaged to serve for a minimum period of six to nine months, a few serving for longer before returning to their medical school to complete their studies and become qualified as doctors. Whenever possible when first commissioned they were given a short preliminary period of training in a hospital ship at Scapa Flow or at the Royal Naval Hospital, Haslar. Haslar received the greater number of these and at times, when a dozen or more young surgeon probationers were received in a 'Batch', as often occurred during the war, some of them coming from medical schools as far afield as Montreal and Toronto and South Africa, they were messed together in one of the large wards of the hospital. They were made temporary members of the wardroom and entitled to make use of the amenities provided, thus being initiated into service customs and naval routine and being partially prepared for going to sea and not feeling as completely at a loss as they might have done had they come direct from civilian life. Considering, however, the number of students who were drafted to ships without any such preliminary period of instruction, they did very well, quickly settling down to the routine on board ship and taking their places as part of the ship's company. Seasickness was to be expected but few allowed this to become a deterrent. One difficulty in many warships, especially destroyers, was that of shortage of cabin accommodation. These ships had not previously carried a doctor or even a sick berth rating. It was the coxswain who formerly assumed responsibility for carrying out such medical duties as existed. When a surgeon probationer was appointed to a ship he was put in charge of the medical stores and became immediately responsible for the care of sick and wounded. In sloops a cabin was usually available but in the cramped conditions of the destroyer the surgeon probationer had to do with slinging a hammock in the wardroom flat (the narrow passage way between the officers' cabins) or more commonly to have arrangements made for his belongings to be stowed in a drawer at the side of the wardroom and to use a cushioned settee on which to sleep at night; this not being possible, however, until the other officers had retired.

The Royal Naval Volunteer Reserve, which originally had not included surgeon probationers, was created in 1903, being divided into Divisions corresponding to the principal ports, i.e. the London (H.M.S. *President*); the Clyde (H.M.S. *Graham*); the Bristol (H.M.S. *Flying Fox*); the Mersey (H.M.S. *Eagle*); the Sussex Division, which had headquarters at Hove; and the Tyne (H.M.S. *Calliope*). The Ulster Division (H.M.S. *Caroline*) was not created until after the war in 1924. The object of the R.N.V.R. was to provide a reserve of officers and men to the Royal Navy and was drawn from the civilian population of Britain. Any experience of shipping and of the sea they had was largely amateur, many of the officers being experienced yachtsmen. When mobilised on the 2nd August, 1914 the R.N.V.R. contributed some 4,800 officers and men to the Royal Navy. But before the end of the war this number had risen to 5,000 officers and 70,000 men.

* * *

The R.N.V.R. contained many fully qualified and experienced doctors in its ranks and through being included in this branch of the service, the surgeon probationers derived certain advantages in having more senior men to whose help they could turn because a number of these were surgeons or physicians on the staff of teaching hospitals in civilian life. Among them one of the foremost was Staff Surgeon R.J. Willan of the Tyne Division. At the time he was lecturer in clinical surgery in Durham University and a surgeon on the staff of the Royal Victoria Infirmary, Newcastle-on-Tyne. He had qualified in medicine with an M.B. and honours in 1906, having won the Gibb Scholarship in pathology and the Charleton in the Principles and Practices of Medicine. When a Division was set up in Newcastle-on-Tyne he had joined and been a keen volunteer from the start, reaching the rank of Staff Surgeon at the outbreak of war. He became attached to the hospital ship *Plassy* at Scapa Flow where he had the opportunity of meeting many newly commissioned surgeon probationers from his own medical school and others, and initiated clinical instruction for them whilst they were waiting to be drafted to their respective ships. Willan was a superb clinical teacher and had the capacity of drawing the young surgeon probationers to him, his informal lectures stressing their importance as representing the medical profession as a whole and confining his talks to the kind of situations, and the complaints, they might expect to encounter in small ships when they had no one to rely on other than themselves. Willan himself was a prolific and experienced writer who had published many articles chiefly relating to the genito-urinary system. Later he became Professor of Surgery in Durham University. All his contributions were characterised by sound and practical common sense, and later in 1939 the seal of approval was accorded him by his surgical confrères when he was elected a Member of Council of the Royal College of Surgeons of England. After the First World War he became Surgeon Captain, R.N.V.R. and was decorated with the V.R.D., the M.V.O., and O.B.E. During the 1914-18 war, whilst serving at Scapa Flow, he was appointed Medical Advisor to young Prince Albert, then serving as a midshipman in one of the battleships of the Grand Fleet. Later, of course, the latter was to become King George VI. Willan also had occasion to treat the Commander-in-Chief, Admiral Lord Jellicoe, and at the conclusion of the war was honoured by being appointed an Honorary Surgeon to King George V.

During his lifetime he received many honours. During the Second World War he was promoted Surgeon Rear-Admiral and became a member of the Naval Medical Consultant Staff. He died in 1955 but his memory is still revered by all who knew him and particularly by those who served as surgeon probationers for whom he had been, not only their acknowledged mentor, but also ever their champion.

Those who remember him and the manner in which he strove to improve the small contribution made by the surgeon probationers during the first World War still bless him for the slim volume which he published under the auspices of the Admiralty: *Clinical Notes for Surgeon Probationers, R.N.V.R.*[1] The writer, who has been a teacher of medical students for some thirty-five years, can recall no other book of that period which contained so much valuable and sound advice condensed into so few pages. It was designed exclusively for young medical students who, faced with a certain amount of responsibility, and being alone in their respective ships, had it to draw on for clinical advice. Of all his writings, in compiling this modest brief work, he achieved his finest hour. The little book, long forgotten, reveals his inspiration as a teacher and deserves a place among the noteworthy works of the past. It is reproduced in full in Part 2.

Contribution of the Belfast Medical School

Conscription to the armed forces was not applied to Ireland as it was to other parts of the United Kingdom, of which it then formed a part, and from both north and south there was a brisk response to the call for recruits on the outbreak of war. The same was true of the medical schools in the country, especially the hospitals associated with Trinity College, Dublin, and the Royal Victoria Hospital, principal teaching hospital of the Queen's University of Belfast. But many students from other medical schools took advantage of the Admiralty's announcement about surgeon probationers by offering their services temporarily. These came from Trinity College, Dublin and those who were studying for the Conjoint Licentiate of the Royal Colleges of Surgeons and of Physicians in Dublin, and from the National University and its colleges in Cork and Galway. At the Queen's University of Belfast an Officer's Training Corps had been formed in 1911-12, its contingent forming part of the Territorial Army and playing an important role in the training and formation of the Ulster Division, which took a prominent place later in the Battle of the Somme in 1916, suffering heavy casualties.[1] But, despite Belfast's international reputation as a shipbuilding centre and the influence of the shipyards of Messrs. Harland and Wolff, and Workman Clark, pre-war there was no naval counterpart of the O.T.C. in the University. Even in 1924, when H.M.S. *Caroline* became the headquarters of the Ulster Division, R.N.V.R., this remained under the control of the Admiralty and the Admiral Commanding Reserves. It is perhaps not without significance, therefore, that some of the earliest entrants to the Division were in the Medical Branch, and were young doctors who had already had experience of seagoing during the war as surgeon probationers.

Among the first students to volunteer from Queen's in Belfast was Robert Hall, better known as 'Robin'. He served for a time in a destroyer in the North Sea early in the war, and at college had had a distinguished record as an athlete, holding the record for the long jump. After returning from the Navy and graduating at Queen's he became Medical Officer to the Post Office in Belfast, and Principal Medical

Victor Millington Synge, Surgeon Probationer, H.M.S. Petrel, recalls an incident during 1917 when his ship, patrolling outside the Firth of Forth, received a signal that a Norwegian ship had left Leith some hours previously without having her papers properly checked. She had a good start and was already well down almost over the horizon when they began chasing her at full speed ahead. 'I volunteered to work in the stoke hold and I had a pain in my back for days afterwards. When we came up with the ship the big letters S.I.F. were legible. In Norwegian, of course, S.I.F. denotes a reef, but to the British, the pox!' Became Regius Professor of Physic, Trinity College, Dublin. Visit. Phys., Royal City of Dublin, Hospital.

Frederick Martin Brice Allen, M.D., F.R.C.P. (Lond.) Professor of Child Health, Queen's University, Belfast. Surgeon Probationer in 1917, later, Surgeon Lieutenant Commander, R.N.V.R.

George Dixon Fisher McFadden, M.Ch., F.R.C.S., Eng., Senior Surgeon, Belfast City and Ulster Hospitals and Consultant Surgeon to Claremont Street Hospital for Nervous Diseases. Surgeon Probationer in 1915/16. The photograph on the left shows him on a stroll between Devonport and Cawsand. The photograph on the right was taken on the quarter deck of his ship and shows the captain, H. Horan, D.S.C., who later became Admiral.

18

Officer of the Ulster Division of the R.N.V.R. after its formation. He served in the Second Great War and attained the rank of Surgeon Captain, R.N.V.R., and became particularly well-known throughout the service, his interest in the Navy always eclipsing all other demands on his time.

His brother, Hugh Edwin Hall (Hugo), was further advanced in his studies at Queen's and did not serve as a surgeon probationer, but when he qualified in 1915 joined the Navy promptly and was for the remainder of the war a Surgeon Lieutenant in H.M.S. *Concord*, a 'C' class cruiser. After the war he also joined the Ulster Division, R.N.V.R. and was appointed to the staff of the Royal Victoria Hospital, where he specialised in venereology. During the Second War he was Principal Medical Officer at the naval base in Londonderry, and later spent some years at sea in the same role as a Surgeon Commander in H.M.S. *Furious*, the well-known aircraft carrier.

It is difficult to trace the names of all the Belfast students who served as surgeon probationers, but among the first to volunteer between 1914-16 were Samuel Acheson, Hugh Paul, William James Lytle, George Percy Storey, Henry Poston, James Browne Wiley and George Dixon Fisher McFadden, all of them students at the Royal Victoria Hospital.

Samuel Acheson, served in H.M.S. *Laverock*, a destroyer based at Harwich in the North Sea. After graduation in 1918 he rejoined the navy as a Surgeon Lieutenant, and subsequently entered into general practice in East Belfast.

Hugh Paul, who served in H.M.S. *Shark* before Jutland, later in another destroyer, H.M.S. *Christopher*. After graduation at Queen's he became Deputy M.O.H. at Oldham, Lancs.

William James Lytle from Maghera, Co. Derry, also served in a destroyer in the North Sea. On return to Queen's he graduated M.B. in 1918 and subsequently took up a surgical career, becoming a consultant on the staff of the Sheffield Royal Infirmary.

George Percy Storey, another Queen's student and an international hockey player, volunteered for the navy in 1915 and served in H.M.S. *Opal* at Scapa Flow with the Grand Fleet. He was drowned in 1917 when his ship was wrecked off the Orkneys. There were only two survivors.

Henry Poston, served in H.M.S. *Linnet*, a destroyer in the North Sea in 1915. He graduated at Queen's in 1919 and subsequently moved to Manchester where he took up orthopaedic surgery, becoming a member of staff at Ancoats Hospital.

James Browne Wiley, a native of Castleblaney, Co. Monaghan, served in H.M.S. *Obedient*, a destroyer with the Grand Fleet, and graduated at Queen's, Belfast in 1920.

George Dixon Fisher McFadden of Newtownstewart, Co. Tyrone. After spending a time at Haslar Hospital, where he contracted typhoid fever, was appointed to H.M.S. *Archer*, at first in the Channel approaches, where he had the extraordinary experience of being washed overboard, and, after being carried some distance away from the side of the ship, washed back on board unhurt except for some minor bruises. Subsequently, his ship was sent to the Mediterranean and he was based at Malta and Mudros, and engaged in convoy escort work. He graduated at Queen's and later became Senior Surgeon to the Belfast City Hospital.

George Storey and George McFadden were close friends. Both did a preliminary period of training at Royal Naval Hospital, Haslar, where McFadden unfortunately took ill with enteric fever. Before leaving to join his ship Storey paid McFadden a visit in hospital, bringing him a pack of cards and teaching him how to play patience. 'It was the last time I saw my friend,' McFadden recalls. Management of a patient with typhoid fever in those days amounted practically to starvation. McFadden remembers how he was given only a small teacup of milk or Horlicks four times a day, nothing else being allowed for weeks. Looking at his legs they appeared wasted as a result, the knee joints standing out so prominently as to resemble Charcot's joints, and when he was allowed out of bed he was unable to stand and had to spend some weeks learning again to walk. After six weeks' sick leave he was appointed to H.M.S. *Archer*, a destroyer stationed in the Firth of Forth at the time and attached to the battle cruisers of the Grand Fleet. Thereafter, his ship was transferred to Plymouth for escort duty and a new captain, Patrick Horan, appointed. It was ▉▉▉ ▉▉▉▉rmy autumn and winter, with frequent gales. McFadden was given as a cabin the use of the tiller flat in the extreme stern of the ship. It was approached from the deck by a steel ladder and a manhole covering and formerly had been used principally as a wine store. As the decks were often swept by seas, in bad weather he found it safer to sleep in the wardroom, placing the dining room chairs side by side with their back and fronts alternating to keep him from rolling off the settee. One night, when conditions seemed more promising, he decided to turn in to his improvised cabin in the tiller flat but some hours later was awakened by a sea pouring down the manhole hatch, which he had left open for ventilation, and decided to retreat to the wardroom: 'I picked up an old dressing gown as an extra and climbed on deck; as I paused to fasten the manhole cover shut I was lifted like a cork and carried on a wave out to sea. I could see the ship silhouetted against the horizon, steaming away about 100 yards distant, although this was difficult to estimate — it might have been about half that... At any rate, I thought this is the end — death cometh sooner or later, and the wardroom will be thinking in the morning that the doctor is having a long sleep. The next thing I remember was seeing a light in the stern of the ship and I realised that I must be close to it. Managing to grab the side, and then striving with kicks of my legs, as the ship rolled over I managed finally to clamber on deck and grab the four-inch gun on the poop, against which I steadied myself. Then I decided to return to the stern flat for dry clothes and made another effort, this time successfully, to gain the wardroom. I think it was the backlash of the sea that had carried me off the deck, which was my salvation but I do not like to think or talk about the episode, though I shall never forget it.'

After a winter spent mostly escorting merchantmen in the approaches to the Channel H.M.S. *Archer* was transferred in May, 1917 to the Mediterranean, a Lieut. Taylor taking over command of the ship from Horan. There she was based at Mudros on the Island of Lemnos in the Aegean and they had the task of patrolling outside the Dardanelles on watch for the appearance of the German battle cruisers *Goeben* and *Breslau*, which were still at large. The ship was also engaged in escort duty from Salonika to Alexandria and he remembers seeing one troopship packed with men of the Ulster Division, including Maynard Sinclair,[2] who ultimately was to become Minister of Finance in the Northern Ireland Government.

Others who qualified in medicine at Queen's and were released to the navy temporarily when they had passed their second M.B. were: a most colourful character named William Caithness, who served in H.M.S. *Opportune* in May 1918, a destroyer with the Grand Fleet, and on return to Belfast graduated in 1920 and later took up general and private hotel practice in the West End of London. I think there were two other students in his year who volunteered similarly but their names escape me. After them came in 1917: Fred Allen, R. L. Dodds, Jimmy Gaussen, Sydney W. T. Lee, Fred Moffitt and Bob Pedlow. Another was named Gallaher, who was in a destroyer which took part in the Battle of Jutland. On that day he was idling in the wardroom when he heard the sound of distant gunfire and, hurrying up the ladder to the quarter-deck, unfortunately lost his balance and fell down backwards. On examination he was found to be suffering from cerebrospinal meningitis and was sent to hospital as soon as this could be arranged, and afterwards was invalided.

Frederick Martin Brice Allen served with the Grand Fleet at Scapa Flow in 1917 as Surgeon Probationer to H.M.S. *Miranda*, and graduated in 1920 at Belfast with honours. Later he became Professor of Child Health at the university and was the author of a well-known book on diseases of children. Following the founding of the Ulster Division of the R.N.V.R. he rejoined and for some years was an active member of the Division.

Robert Leslie Dodds, who also served with the Grand Fleet as Surgeon Probationer to H.M.S. *Mameluke*, graduated at Queen's in 1920 and subsequently took up gynaecology and obstetrics until his premature death as a comparatively young man. I remember he told me that he had been sorely troubled by seasickness.

James Frederick Herbert Gaussen graduated in Belfast in 1921 and after the war re-entered the Royal Navy as Surgeon Lieutenant, making it his career and subsequently attaining the rank of Surgeon Captain.

Sydney William Timpson Lee of Ahoghill, Co. Antrim, who served in 1917 as Surgeon Probationer in a sloop, H.M.S. *Rosemary*, later graduated M.B. in 1920, taking up a career in the Colonial Medical Service in East Africa.

Frederick William Moffitt, who served as a Surgeon Probationer in 1917 in H.M.S. *Gurka*, a destroyer at Scapa Flow attached to the Grand Fleet, after graduation in Belfast went into general practice there.

Robert Pedlow who served in H.M.S. *Medea* as Surgeon Probationer, graduated in Belfast in 1923, later going into general practice in Lurgan.

At this stage of the war my own year had only completed their first medical examination and begun to prepare for the second in anatomy and physiology. I remember in the zoology classes Professor Gregg Wilson giving a fiery address on the need for us to consider our duty to our country and to volunteer for the army without delay. He appealed to our patriotism in a manner not unlike that described by Remarque in his well-known book *All Quiet on the Western Front*, but I was determined to stay on at Queen's for another year when I should be nineteen and ready to offer my services as a surgeon probationer. Those of us who knew many of the returning veterans, both from the army and the navy, who had resumed their studies and come into our year, could not fail to notice the change that had taken place in them as a result of their experiences. Not only did they settle down to work much more easily, but they exuded a confident attitude and self-assurance that we did not possess. The ex-surgeon probationers were especially notable for their panache. For example, speaking of his experiences in the destroyer *Mameluke*, Leslie Dodds gave a wry smile and said he could recall only an incident which had occurred one stormy night in winter in the North Sea when his ship was ploughing through a heavy sea and he was being dreadfully sick. From his couch on the wardroom settee, however, in the middle of the night he was called on deck to attend to a seaman who had fallen and fractured his shoulder. There was little he could do except ease the man's pain by giving him ¼ gr. of morphine, and put on temporary splints until they got back to Scapa the next day, when he sent the man to hospital. All returning students who had served in the forces received a little badge which they proudly wore in their button-holes, and especially at examination time this proved of great value for they received special consideration from the examiners.

At Queen's, clinical work was not begun at the hospital until the commencement of the third year. A year later, in June 1918, when many of us had passed the second M.B. and volunteered for the navy, we spent the few weeks intervening before we received our appointments in clinical work at hospital, learning to dress cuts and bruises, to apply bandages, and to carry out other minor tasks under the direction of the house surgeon, one Sam Acheson, who himself had returned from seagoing and was on the point of graduating now and re-entering the navy as a Surgeon Lieutenant.

Our position, indeed, was very similar to that of surgeon probationer Stanley Sykes.[3] He remembers how gratified he was to be promoted to the title of 'doctor' as soon as he stepped on board his ship, and how he found two chests of medicine and drugs and a generous supply of surgical dressings, with a few instruments, sutures, clinical thermometers, and a hypodermic syringe with a bottle of morphine solution, together with a small steriliser. He was well prepared for treating every day cuts and burns but found it not possible to do much in the way of medical treatment. One difficulty lay in their being no sick bay, consultations for treatment having to be given in the upper deck or in the dark duffle suit store which was cold and damp. If water was required it had to be fetched in a basin from the galley and he had, of course, no sick berth staff to assist him. He had tried sleeping in the lobby or wardroom in a hammock but this often hit the stove pipe so violently on one side and afterwards rebounded against the rifle rack on the other side that in time he gave up sleeping in a hammock, preferring one of the wardroom settees. One night, however, when he forgot to raise the bunk-board he found himself shot off on to the deck with his head in the fireplace. He followed the approved plan of giving lectures on first-aid to the ship's company, these taking place during working hours because it was impossible to arouse any interest in the men during their leisure period of 'make and mend'. In these lectures he tried to show them how to recognise a fracture and in dealing with burns how to apply picric acid dressings. The majority of the cases he saw in his ship were of colds, coughs, cuts, burns and bruises. Constipation was a frequent complaint and attributed to the lack of exercise and shortage of vegetables, but shortly after commissioning there was an outbreak of diarrhoea which was put down to contamination of the water supply. There were two cases of scabies, one of secondary syphillis, one of gonnorhoea, and two of impetigo. He had to send one man to the depot ship with an inguinal hernia which was on the point of becoming strangulated. He found the little glass tubes supplied with needles already threaded and sterilised excellent for dealing with bad cuts and, in spite of the difficulty in ensuring aseptic operating conditions, suppurating fingers, thrombosed piles, boils and whitlows all progressed satisfactorily.

In another short article by Surgeon Probationer S. H. Waddy published in the *Journal of the Royal Naval Medical Service* 1918 he mentions that he had been appointed to a destroyer of the latest type. At night he slept on one of the wardroom settees and on the coxswain's suggestion a small sick bay was provided for him by conversion of the drying room under the break of the fo'c'sle. This space, not more than a few feet square, was big enough to hold the medical stores, sterilising instruments and tubes of Nargol jelly and calomel cream, together with a bottle of mist, pectoral, lead lotion, and tablets of potassium permanganate. Each bottle was held in position in a wooden square so that in bad weather it did not break or spill. In the corner was a strong shelf to which a Neil Robertson stretcher was affixed against the after bulkhead. First aid bags were hung on the bulkheads by hooks, ready for distribution to the chief points where injuries from wounding might be expected.

Periodically the ship's company was inspected and a gargling routine instituted. Once when a suspected case of cerebrospinal meningitis was discovered the messdecks were washed down with a solution of Izal.

Both Mr. Sykes and Mr. Waddy refer to the discovery of rats, Waddy pointing out that their presence was regarded by the sailors as being a good omen. When one of them was asked what would happen if a rat were killed on board he declared, 'That means we are going into action, Sir.' Both writers spoke kindly of their experiences at sea which they were sure gave them an understanding of human nature as well as satisfying to some extent their nomadic instincts. 'It had been a pleasant change for a medical student, proverbially impecunious, to be paid to learn as an officer, after years of paying to be taught as a student.'

To revert to Belfast students. Unlike our predecessors during the war, most of whom were drafted to ships based at Scapa Flow, the Forth of Clyde, Harwich, or the Dover Patrol, the majority of the surgeon probationers in my year seem to have been appointed overseas to destroyers or sloops in the Mediterranean. There were:-

John Hubert Dunn, who had been a student in the year before us and who waited until he had entered his third year before volunteering, entering the navy late in 1917 and was drafted to a destroyer stationed at Scapa Flow, H.M.S. *Triton*, in which he served through part of 1918.

Afterwards, he humorously described his position in the ship as being the 'lowest form of medical-nautical life'. After graduation and holding the offices of house physician at the Belfast Infirmary and Greenwich Hospital, he became R.M.O. to the National Heart Hospital, and later between the wars became a well-known physician in London, engaged in hotel practice. In the second war he served overseas again, this time in the Army with the rank of Lieutenant Colonel, T.A., being Medical Adviser at one time to the Malta Command, and being awarded the O.B.E.

Arthur Hugh McCulloch Eaton served in a sloop, H.M.S. *Honeysuckle*, in the Mediterranean, based at Malta. He graduated in Belfast in 1922 and ultimately became Consulting Surgeon to the Tyrone County Hospital, Omagh. We had some good times together at Malta, and were good friends.

Thomas Howard Crozier also served in the Mediterranean in a sloop in 1918-19, H.M.S. *Lobelia*. He qualified M.B. in 1921 at Belfast and later became Consulting Physician on the staff of the City Hospital, Belfast and Royal Victoria Hospital. In the Second World War he served with the army in the Middle East with the rank of Lieutenant Colonel, R.A.M.C.

John Scott Lyle, a doctor's son, who came from Newtownstewart, Co. Tyrone entered the navy in 1918, and after spending a short period at the Royal Naval Hospital, Haslar, became surgeon probationer to H.M.S. *Alarm*, a destroyer. He graduated at Queen's in 1922 and later went into general practice.

William McCartan of Castlewellan, Co. Down, who graduated in 1922, served a time as surgeon probationer to a sloop, H.M.S. *Pentstemon*, in the Mediterranean, seeing service in the Levant, in co-operation with the military forces under General Allenby, subsequently became Medical Officer-in-Charge of the Sussex County Hospital, Haywards Health, Sussex.

Richard Sydney Allison, a close friend of McCartan, served in H.M.S. *Acorn*, a destroyer in the Mediterranean.

William Alexander Beck was appointed to Haslar along with Allison and Lyle, and later drafted to H.M.S. *Rifleman*, a destroyer of the same flotilla as *Acorn*. He graduated in Belfast in 1921 and went into general practice in the city.

Walter Lascelles. The name of his ship is not known but he volunteered in the latter half of 1918 and served for a time at sea, subsequently returning to qualify in Belfast in 1922, and later going into general practice.

John Herbert Duke was surgeon probationer to the destroyer, H.M.S. *Vendetta*, and served in the North Sea with the Grand Fleet. He qualified in 1921 and subsequently held appointments as Consulting Physician in Geriatric Medicine at St. Andrew's Hospital, Bow, London.

William Aiken Browne was surgeon probationer to H.M.S. *Versatile*, a destroyer, in 1918. He graduated in 1922 and ultimately became Senior Administrative Medical Officer, Northern Ireland Hospitals Authority.

There are at least three other names of medical students at Queen's who served in the last year of the war, but details of whom I have been unable to trace. They were: *W. E. Beck*, who served in the destroyer, H.M.S. *Obdurate*, and later went into general practice in Belfast; *Charles Ronald Christian*, who served in the sloop, H.M.S. *Cyclamen*, and *Robert Johnston*, who served in the armed yacht, H.M.S. *Campanula*, both qualifying in 1921 or 1922.

1. After the war a University Services' Club was formed to include all students who had served with the Forces, and this included a small number of surgeon probationers. An annual dinner was instituted and held each year in the university on the 11th November. The late Dr. Robert Marshall published a short account of the history of the club on the 50th anniversary of its foundation, 1968.

2. Maynard Sinclair was lost in 1953, when the *Princess Victoria*, the Larne/Stranraer ferry was sunk during a great gale.

3. (*J. Roy. Nav. Med. Serv.*, Vol. 3, 1917). When he arrived on board his first ship he described himself as 'a land lover of the deepest dye, never having seen warships before except on a cigarette picture card and my sea experience being confined to four cross-channel journeys'.

The Surgeon Probationers In Action

In the First Great War it was uncommon for ships to experience frequent bouts of action with enemy vessels (apart from submarines). At the Battle of Jutland — fought on the 31st May, 1916 — the majority of the seventy or eighty British destroyers involved were staffed by surgeon probationers. Cerebrospinal meningitis was prevalent in the Fleet in that year and surgeon probationer A. E. W. Gallaher's experience has already been recounted.

Of the destroyers taking part in the battle, part of them were attached to the battleships of the Grand Fleet based at Scapa Flow and the others mainly were from the Forth and attendant on the battle cruisers. The 4th flotilla, which included H.M.S. *Tipperary, Acasta, Achates, Ardent, Ambuscade, Fortune, Shark, Spitfire*, and many other destroyers came under heavy enemy gunfire, H.M.S. *Tipperary* being put out of action after being in contact with some enemy four-funnelled cruisers, and being hit by a German salvo, a heavy and accurate fire being directed on her until finally she burst into flames and was left a blazing wreck until she sank. Meanwhile, other ships notably *Spitfire*, had been under severe attack, as also *Broke*, the latter as a result of crashing into her next astern, *Sparrowhawk*, had had her stern blown off and was abandoned as a helpless wreck before she sank. Other ships of the flotilla which suffered severely during the fighting were *Fortune* and *Ardent*, both being sunk. Of H.M.S. *Ardent's* crew there were only two survivors, and from the *Fortune* only two raft loads of survivors were rescued.

Altogether in the battle there was a total of 6,685 casualties, composed of 363 officers and 6,322 men.[1] In the destroyers alone 38 officers and 483 men were killed; 8 officers and 76 men wounded; and 9 officers and 150 men taken prisoners-of-war.

Ship	Killed Officers	Men	Wounded Officers	Men	Prisoners-of-war Officers	Men
H.M.S. *Acasta*	1	5	-	-	-	-
H.M.S. *Ardent* (sunk)	4	74	1	1	-	-

Ship	Killed Officers	Killed Men	Wounded Officers	Wounded Men	Prisoners-of-war Officers	Prisoners-of-war Men
H.M.S. *Broke*	1	46	3	33	-	-
H.M.S. *Fortune* (sunk)	4	63	-	1	-	-
H.M.S. *Moorsom*	-	-	-	1	-	-
H.M.S. *Nessus*	2	5	-	7	-	-
H.M.S. *Nestor* (sunk)	2	5	-	-	5	74
H.M.S. *Nomad* (sunk)	1	7	-	-	4	68
H.M.S. *Onslaught*	3	2	-	2	-	-
H.M.S. *Onslow*	-	2	-	3	-	-
H.M.S. *Petard*	2	7	1	5	-	-
H.M.S. *Porpoise*	-	2	-	2	-	-
H.M.S. *Shark* (sunk)	7	79	-	2	-	-
H.M.S. *Sparrowhawk* (sunk)	-	6	-	-	-	-
H.M.S. *Spitfire*	-	6	3	16	-	-
H.M.S. *Tipperary* (sunk)	11	174	-	2	-	8
Total	38	483	8	76	9	150

From these official figures for casualties among the destroyers it will be obvious that the surgeon probationers who were entirely alone in their respective ships, having no other medical assistance, were kept busy during and after the action, dressing and attending to the wounded. Taken prisoner-of-war was the surgeon probationer of the *Tipperary* who was picked up on a life raft by a German ship and taken to Holland in a Dutch trawler. He had been wounded in the leg during the action.

In *Onslaught*, which was the rear ship of the 1st Division of the 12th Flotilla, the captain was badly wounded, the 1st Lieutenant, coxswain and one signalman were killed, and the surgeon probationer kept fully engaged attending to the wounded. All his efforts, however, failed to save the captain, who died of his wounds about noon of that day.

Another ship, H.M.S. *Petard*, was hit six times by shells, one of which penetrated the deckhead of No. 2 stokehold and cut an oil fuel pipe, setting oil alight. Luckily, the engine-room department were able to shut off the oil to the broken pipe and extinguish the fire in a few minutes. The enemy's first salvo had hit the after part of the ship and killed or severely wounded the whole of the officers and crew of the after 4-inch gun. This salvo also wrecked all the officers' cabins and unfortunately killed the surgeon probationer, just at the moment when his services were most required. It was not until daybreak that the surgeon probationer of H.M.S. *Nicator* could go over to the damaged *Petard* to give assistance, but nevertheless with only a destroyer's medical outfit and no anaesthetics he performed wonders and undoubtedly saved a number of lives.

After an attempt by a German cruiser to ram H.M.S. *Spitfire*, and the loss of her foremast, with fire breaking out, the crew stood by and attempted to deal with the situation by the use of fire pumps. Few instances of individual bravery are recorded but that of the surgeon probationer of the *Spitfire*, *Mr. Douglas George Patrick Bell*, was exceptional. In the official citation in the *London Gazette* for 15th September, 1916, (Supplement), it states 'Surgeon Probationer Douglas George Patrick Bell, R.N.V.R. devoted great attention to the wounded, and amputated a limb single-handed in the dark.' A student, aged nineteen, of the Newcastle Medical School, and the son of a Fellow of the Royal Society of Edinburgh and born at Fulforth in Co. Durham, another official account after the battle commented on what fine work he had done. The amputee was an able seaman who had been found with the coxswain amongst the wreckage of the bridge and it was the former's leg which Bell amputated, without the aid of any anaesthetic. Whilst he was performing the operation the fire party was busy all round him with their fire hoses. Another official comment says about him: 'It was marvellous the way this young doctor moved about, eventually getting all the wounded into the wardroom and cabins, and he never left them or took any rest himself until the ship arrived in harbour some 36 hours later.'

After the battle he contributed an account to the University of Durham College of Medicine expressing the hope that his own impression of the action 'may not be uninteresting'.

'Wednesday, 31st May was a lovely day with the sun shining from a practically cloudless sky and the sea almost calm or motionless, the horizon being surrounded by a haze. In *Spitfire*, until about 7 bells in the afternoon watch (3.30 p.m.), like most of our days at sea we spent in eating and sleeping, interspersed with some desultory reading and an occasional walk up and down the quarter-deck, admiring the magnificent sight of the squadrons of the Grand Fleet at sea... I was just about to retire to the wardroom for seven-bell tea when I noticed an unusual number of signals flying from the *Iron Duke*, on whose port bow we were. The whole fleet increased speed to about 20 knots and confirmation that something unusual was occurring was obtained by a wireless message from the flagship announcing that our battle cruiser squadron was pursuing a German battle cruiser squadron and expecting to come up with them... At 4.10 p.m. we received another wireless message which said that our battle cruisers were engaging the enemy... Shortly after this we took in the news that our 5th battle squadron was engaged with the German High Sea Fleet.'

As the ship went to action stations the captain relieved the 1st lieutenant on the bridge and the latter took up his station in command of the after-gun. Meanwhile, Bell had a message from the bridge to get his bandages and instruments ready, but he had them already distributed in first-aid bags near to every spot likely to have casualties, with picric acid dressings in the engine and boiler rooms. He carried another bag with a shoulder strap, which had a hypodermic syringe in a case, an instrument valise, tourniquets... He also unearthed some empty gin bottles, which he had had filled with 1-20 carbolic. This was all the antiseptic he possessed because the service bottle of iodine had been tossed overboard before by the 1st lieutenant after Bell, 'in a moment of waywardness,' had painted his somewhat bald head because he had found the cervical glands enlarged.

Bell's account in the journal gives a good description of the battle, but of his own part in it he says little. To continue:

'The noise of the firing was indescribable, the hackneyed expression, thunder of the guns, conveys very little idea of the real thing. The whole show seemed one great pandemonium to a novice at sea-fighting. However, being on the disengaged side of the fleet we were in no particular danger, save from a few stray ''overs'' which were dropping here and there among the flotilla.

'After about half-an-hour or more the huns seemed to evade us in the mist and the terrific battering subsided somewhat, only to break out again with renewed vigour at intervals throughout the night. When opportunity offered between the ringings of the alarm gong, we all tore up on deck and refreshed ourselves with sandwiches and cocoa.

'Up till about 11.30 p.m. the action was a most enjoyable sight and a great experience. At this hour, however, our flotilla went in to attack

31

some German battleships and it now became too awful to be at all enjoyable. We were second in the line and in the 1st division of four, the order being *Tipperary*, *Spitfire*, *Sparrowhawk* and *Fortune*, three out of the four ships in the 1st division being sunk and only *Spitfire* surviving.

'We attacked, following the *Tipperary*, at about 28 knots; on getting close to the enemy we fired two torpedoes at practically point blank range of 800 yards. It was observed to explode all right and the vessel heeled over and sank... We passed the *Tipperary*, which was a ghastly sight — one mass of red, hot metal from bow to stern. She sank in about a minute. We were now close up to the hun, which had done for our leader (*Tipperary*) and at the moment when a collision seemed imminent she loosed off an eleven-inch shell at our bridge, causing its total destruction and the death of our signalman and quarter-master and the wounding of all the others.

'The First Lieutenant now took command since the Captain was laid out among the debris. He got the after-steering gear connected up and we had just missed another hun battleship on our stern by what seemed inches, her guns seeming to hang over our quarter-deck and the only reason for not being blown out of the way was that the enemy could not depress the elevation of the guns enough to hit us.

'We now had time to look at our damage. We had six men killed and nineteen wounded and a very badly smashed ship. The engineer officer got to work patching up holes and shoring up bulk heads, etc. and the remains of the torpedo party set about correcting the vagaries of the electrical circuits throughout the ship. The removal of the wounded was very difficult as anyone touching metal railings or the super-structure got a terrific ''earth'', emanating chiefly I believe from the tangled wireless aerials.

'After a time the captain came to and was ready to resume command The chief damage was various lacerations, black eyes, thick ears, etc. and he kept us on a north-westerly course for about three hours when the sea got up into a very heavy swell and the only course we could manage was directly south. All Thursday we struggled south at 6 knots but as all our charts had been lost with the bridge we had no definite idea where they were, except somewhere on the eastern side of the Dogger Bank.'

Such an experience as that of young Mr. Bell showed that untried medical students were able to play a useful part and display the same bravery in action as did their more experienced shipmates. On returning to his studies Mr. Bell in due course graduated M.B., B.S. with honours in Durham University in 1919. There he was awarded the Charlton, Goyder and Philipson Scholarships, in the last-named obtaining the highest marks in his final professional year. Four years later he proceeded to the M.D. and after holding appointments at the Royal Victoria Infirmary, Newcastle-on-Tyne, finally went into general practice at Throckley, near Newburn-on-Tyne. He was employed on full-time service with the Ministry of Pensions towards the end of his time in practice, and after the Second World War eventually became Deputy Commissioner for Medical Services in this region. He died on 30th January, 1959 aged sixty-two years. A colleague wrote of him: ' "D.G.P.", as he was known to all his friends, seemed to have all the attributes which make for success... He was extremely handsome, and he and his wife were outstanding at any social function... An excellent sportsman, he loved the country life and open spaces, and much enjoyed a day amidst the grouse and pheasants.' His wife, Kathleen M. Weldon, predeceased him by a few days, and they left a son and daughter.

Earlier, as a result of the Dogger Bank action, *Mr. James Alexander Stirling* had been awarded the D.S.C. for outstanding bravery. He was surgeon probationer and serving in H.M. destroyer *Meteor*, and a student at Edinburgh University. On returning to complete his studies, he was elected President of the Student's Representative Council and graduated M.B., B.Ch. in 1919. After holding house appointments and taking the D.P.H. he worked as medical officer to the County Councils of Kincardine, Cumberland and Durham, and for the Boroughs of Hartlepool and finally Chesterfield. He was interested in Derbyshire County Cricket Club, and in medico-political affairs, becoming chairman of the Chesterfield Division of the B.M.A. and was enrolled as a Fellow of the B.M.A. 'A friend to everyone, he had no enemies, although he could wax quite vituperative when a cricketer missed an easy catch or show some other streak of lethargy during a game.' He died in 1971 at the age of seventy-seven, after a long illness, and was survived by his wife and daughter.

Another notable occasion was the action fought between British and enemy destroyers in the Channel in December, 1917. The ships engaged were *Swift* and *Broke*, and their surgeon probationers were respectively *J. S. Westwater* and *Christopher Thomas Helsham*, both of

33

whom were awarded the D.S.C. for their gallantry under fire. *Swift* had one man killed and five wounded, and *Broke* suffered more heavily, losing 21 killed and 24 wounded, most of them by a shell which burst in the boiler room. The Commanding Officer of *Broke* was Edward Ratcliffe Evans, C.B., who was afterwards promoted to Captain and subsequently Admiral, and awarded the D.S.O. This destroyer action was notable because it was not until February, 1918 that enemy destroyers again ventured into the straits. I have been unable to trace the subsequent history of Mr. Westwater, but as regards Mr. C. T. Helsham, he graduated at Newcastle and Guy's Hospital, obtaining the M.R.C.S., L.R.C.P. in 1919. Afterwards he was appointed to the local hospital and wrote an account of an unusual case of strangulated scrotal hernia with volvulus of the small intestine in the inguinal canal. (B.M.J. 1921). He died in 1934 at the premature age of thirty-nine.

Another surgeon probationer who was awarded the D.S.C. in 1915 for conspicuous bravery, served in a 'Q' ship under the famous Admiral Gordon Campbell, V.C. This was *Mr. Alexander Coutts Fowler*. A native of Aberdeen, he graduated M.B., Ch.B. in 1919 and M.D. in 1923. On his return he was Resident Medical Officer in the Royal Hospital for Sick Children, Aberdeen and later became Resident Medical Officer of the Tor-na-Dee Sanatorium for pulmonary tuberculosis. He obtained in 1924 the Diploma of Medical Radiology and Electricity at Cambridge, and later returned to Aberdeen when he was appointed honorary assistant radiologist to the Royal Hospital for Sick Children, and radiologist to the Kepplestone and Armstrong nursing homes. Unfortunately, for years he was in ill-health and died at the early age of thirty-eight. His loss was greatly mourned. Thus, one of the numerous wreaths laid at his funeral bore the inscription 'To a gallant shipmate'. To his friends he was always known for his gentleness and humility of character, and his indifference to personal gain or praise although his many acts of charity and kindliness were well-known. He died unmarried.

The last medical student to be awarded the D.S.C. whilst serving as surgeon probationer during the war was *George Edward Strahan* of H.M.S. *Stork*. After the war he emigrated to Southern Rhodesia where he held a post in the Government Medical Service. An L.R.C.P.I. and L.M., L.R.C.S.I. and M. he graduated in 1921 in Dublin and for a time held a house appointment in the Croydon General Hospital.

Short decisive actions were fought between British destroyers and the

German light cruisers, *Bremner* and *Bremse*, which attached the convoy they were escorting across the North Sea from Norway to Britain. On the first occasion when H.M.S. *Strongbow* and *Mary Rose* were lost, both surgeon probationers perished in the action, the death of Ivan C. Barclay of *Mary Rose* being reported officially. On another similar occasion that winter, when in the course of an attack on a convoy, H.M.S. *Partridge* was sunk, the surgeon probationer, Mr. Peter Alexander Faichney was rescued from the water and taken prisoner-of-war. He had been serving in the ship since July 1917 and was due for demobilisation early in the year 1918, but in December 1917 his demobilisation was rescinded because he had been picked up, taken prisoner, and incarcerated in Holland. Steps were taken by the Admiralty in March 1918 to have his position reviewed on account of his being a medical student and he was repatriated on the 22nd March, after some months. In April 1918 his demobilisation was completed and his case favourably reviewed by the Medical Director General and the Dean of Glasgow University concurring, he was freed to resume his studies, qualifying M.B., B.Ch. in 1921.

Another medical student, George F. Abercrombie, who had experience in action[2] was from Cambridge and Barts. Subsequently, he was awarded the V.R.D. and became a prominent member of the London Division. In the Second World War he was P.M.O. of H.M.S. *Anson*, his last appointment in the service, and was promoted Surgeon Captain, R.N.V.R. He had, therefore, the rare distinction of serving in all the ranks open to medical men in the R.N.V.R. He became a surgeon probationer in September 1917, and after passing his second M.B. and with only three months' clinical experience in dressing at Addenbrooke's Hospital, served in five different destroyers: H.M.S. *Onslaught, Lightfoot, Velox, Warwick* and *Trident. Warwick* was selected by Admiral Keys as his flagship for the operations against Zeebrugge and Ostend in April 1918, and Abercrombie recounts:

'We, therefore, sailed on St. George's Eve, *Vindictive* being due alongside the mole at Zeebrugge at midnight. As we approached under cover of a smokescreen which concealed us and protected us from the remarkably brilliant German star-shell, a certain amount of patter was heard of falling metal fragments; the Sub-Lieutenant and I, standing together near the torpedo tubes, looked at each other and agreed that it was time we took cover. About an hour later I got a momentary glimpse of *Vindictive* coming away, and shortly after that we came upon a most awe-inspiring sight, a motor launch so overcrowded with men that it seemed likely she might capsize at any moment. She managed to get alongside, there was a call for stretchers, and she transferred to us 101 survivors from the block-ships *Intrepid* and *Iphigenia*.

'When the first casualty arrived on our deck, two men lifted the stretcher and said to me, "Where to, Sir?" There was only one place to go and that was the mess deck under the fo'c'sle, a comparatively large space, undivided. Of those brought on board, three were dead and 31 others were casualties. There was a group of 10 or 11 who puzzled me. They were in some distress, with pain in the chest and a cough, and I wondered what this could be. It occurred to me that they were gassed, but by what I did not know. I thought it was possible that fumes from the explosives used to sink the blockships might have caused this. The Admiral sent his Flag-Lieutenant, Vaughan Morgan, down to the mess deck to help me, and his help was really magnificent. "What shall we do for these men?" he said. A line from Bainbridge & Menzies' *Physiology* had come back to me to the effect that, if one made a man vomit with an emetic, one emptied not only his stomach but also his lungs. "Make them vomit," I said. "How?" he said. "Mustard and water," said I. "How strong?" "Oh, pretty strong," said I, feeling it must be all or nothing.

'... The other casualties, some eighteen or twenty, who had been caught by machine-gun fire on their way out of harbour in the motor launch now lay on the mess tables and benches and on the deck itself under the fo'c'sle. We did what we could for them, dressing their wounds, giving them morphine in full doses, making them as comfortable as we could with blankets, cocoa and so on. Some time early in the morning when I straightened up from leaning over a man, I found the Admiral at my elbow, and he and his Captain D then went round the mess deck talking to everyone, cheering them up wonderfully and telling them that their work was one of the finest things in history.'

In the last years of the war the British and Italians maintained an anti-submarine barrage to prevent German submarines gaining access to the Mediterranean, through the Straits of Gibraltar and Otranto. In the Adriatic this extended across the Straits and consisted of several lines of trawlers, sloops, kite balloons and destroyers. One night two Austrian cruisers came down on the barrage at midnight and sank a number of drifters, damaging a destroyer, H.M.S. *Hornet*, and sank another,

H.M.S. *Phoenix*. The surgeon probationer of the latter ship was a William Balfour and he was killed in the action.

1. *The Fighting at Jutland* — The Personal Experiences of Sixty Officers and Men of the British Fleet. Printed by MacDonald & Co., Glasgow.

2. See 'Naval Occasions', *Jnl. Med. Digest,* Vol. 19, No. 3. March, 1974. p. 69-70.

Some Reminiscences of the R.N. Hospital, Haslar, in 1918

This chapter and the next are based on a diary kept over the eight months in 1918-19 when I served as surgeon probationer to the destroyer H.M.S. *Acorn*, then attached to the 5th flotilla and based at Brindisi in the Adriatic. The ship was of some 760 tons burden, oil driven, with twin screws, and carried an armament of two four-inch guns openly mounted on the fo'c'sle and quarter-deck respectively, a light twelve-pounder placed on either side of the break of the fo'c'sle, and two torpedo tubes. In addition, she had a number of depth charges placed aft over the stern, with a light crane on either side from which paravanes could be launched and streamed behind the ship when operating in a minefield. The distinctive features of this 'H' class of destroyer were their one long and two short funnels, open bridge, and guns without shields. The ship's boats consisted of a whaler, dinghy, and a standard type of motor-boat. Besides this *Acorn* had the usual complement of Carley Floats or life rafts. Speed at full throttle was 27 knots. She had been built in 1910-11.

I passed the second M.B. examination in June, 1918 in anatomy and physiology and, having undergone a medical examination, reported for duty on the 31st July, 1918 at the Royal Naval Hospital, Haslar. There, to my surprise, I found that another Belfast medical student, J. S. Lyle and myself were the only two surgeon probationers from the British Isles, all the others, some 15-20 of them, being Canadian, and students at McGill University and La Salle University, Montreal, or from Toronto. For accommodation our batch was lodged in one of the upper wards of the hospital and we were permitted to make use of the wardroom in the medical mess and have our meals there in company of the medical officers.

Being only nineteen years old and having never before been away from home apart from brief holidays, and being educated at a day school, it was a novel experience to find oneself sleeping in a dormitory at night with so many strangers. Not only was their accent and phraseology different but the French Canadians among them would often, when talking together, break into French and had greater fluency of speech in that language. They were two or three years older than us, more easy in their manners and already had some experience of hospital. Certainly, compared to myself, J. S. Lyle and W. A. Beck, also from Belfast, who was shortly to join us at Haslar, the Canadian surgeon probationers seemed to possess infinitely more worldliness and know-how than we did and we never had any difficulty in making friends with them.

Haslar was, of course, a good mixing ground and I noted that it stood in about 60 acres of well-kept grounds and on the sea front overlooking Spithead. It had long roomy corridors with paved cloisters on the ground floor... At dinner in the mess the president, sitting at the top of the long table, and the vice-president, (a junior member of the mess) at the lower end, struck the table with his mallet to call the officers to attention and, raising his glass, looked down the table and announced simply 'Mr. Vice', whereupon the vice-president echoed 'Gentlemen, The King', and the assembled company, raising their glasses, honoured the Toast, all remaining seated, unlike the custom in the Army when all stand for it.[1]

On the 4th August is the note: 'We have decided to apply for service in the Mediterranean... Meanwhile, our mornings are given over to work in the medical wards under the direction of a surgeon named Porteous (a very nice fellow, who played the piano well). On the 10th August we spent the whole morning in the venereal diseases wards and saw as much clinical evidence of syphilis and gonorrhoea as it was possible to include in the time. There was certainly no dearth of material: large gummatous tumours eroding the bones of the skull and presenting on the surface of the scalp as messy open sores; similar ulcers on the legs, a patient with a bulging intra-thoracic aneurysm which had partly eroded his sternum. On another morning when Lyle and I went to the nervous diseases block I saw my first case of tabes, and others of general paralysis of the insane, as well as purely neurotic or mental patients, some of them obvious malingerers, of which one especially remains in my memory.

This was a young sailor with an hysterical or feigned contraction of the muscles of his back. His ship had been blown up and sunk by a mine and the man had developed as a result a permanent stooping or bent posture until he came under the care of Dr. Hildred Carlill,[2] then a Staff Surgeon, R.N. We watched his treatment with amazement. Connecting him to a Faradic battery of the roller type, he told the man to expect the treatment to be painful but that it would certainly cure him, and then proceeded to expose his back and run the Faradic battery up and down the surface of the skin close to the spinal column so that the patient instantly responded by convulsive jerks of the muscles of his back. Before the session had terminated he was able to stand naturally in the erect posture and move his back freely despite his protests that such movements caused pain. The first stage of his recovery had been successfully completed and Carlill predicted that very soon he would be fit for duty again.

On another morning a Fleet Surgeon gave us instruction in the library on naval etiquette and customs, and on the 6th August we were taken around on a visit to H.M.S. *Victory*, which then, in 1918, was still afloat and moored in Portsmouth Harbour. I noted that: 'the main mast of the ship is 365 feet tall and it has five decks. Stored under the poop is the 'chaloupe'' or light open boat which conveyed Admiral Nelson's coffin from the Thames to lie in state in St. Paul's 113 years ago. We were shown too, the exact spot on the quarterdeck where the Admiral had been shot down by a bullet, fired by a French marine from the rigging of the *Redoubtable*.'

Having gained a general impression of the hospital and the work I gravitated to the operating theatre block where I spent many mornings watching operations and received instruction in anaesthetics from one of the senior surgeons of whom 'Fleet Surgeon Morris is one of the decentest (sic) and squarest brass hats I know'. The method in use was a rag and bottle with chloroform and ether. Apparently, many of the younger surgeons had little experience of even this elementary form of anaesthesia for on one occasion, when a burly, red-faced stoker was placed on the table to have an operation for the cure of an inguinal hernia, and the assisting anaesthetist commenced dropping ether on to a gauze mask held over the man's face, he wrongly assumed that the anaesthetic was having effect and told the surgeon he could commence the operation. But as soon as the latter took up a scalpel and touched the man's skin with its cutting edge, he promptly jumped up on the table, and throwing off the preparatory towels, abused the staff with a choice series of oaths and imprecations whilst he struggled with sick berth attendants and surgeon probationers to hold him down by force. Indeed, it took several minutes of prolonged induction by chloroform to bring about the necessary degree of anaesthesia and muscular relaxation so that the operation could proceed.

Life at Haslar, although it lasted only a few weeks was never dull. We could sample the drinks available in the medical mess and shore leave into Portsmouth was granted on most afternoons. I remember that an A.F.O.[3] appeared on the notice board dealing with the behaviour of officers stationed in shore establishments, pointing out that shore leave should not be permitted until 1400 hours. Officers were to be properly dressed, to carry kid gloves, and a regulation cane. Pipe or cigarette smoking was not approved in the streets. In those days one had the choice of the regular public ferry which ran from Gosport to Portsmouth. Most of us preferred the duty picket boat which left the hospital from the end of the jetty leading down to the waterside from the main gate and which was lined by trees and had traversing rails let into the concrete surface so that patients could be conveyed from boats direct by a horse-drawn tramway into the hospital. On such journeys across the harbour attention was paid to seniority, Fleet Surgeons, Staff Surgeons and other senior officers entering the boat after all lower ranks, i.e. S.B.A.s, nurses, V.A.D.s and surgeon probationers were already seated.

One afternoon when with Billy Beck I took a walk over to Lee-on-Solent, it was inspiring to see the young pilots of the embryonic Fleet Air Arm taking up their aircraft, either monoplanes or biplanes, with accommodation for two persons at most. I remember one night after dark returning to Haslar to find 'planes still flying, practising landing and taking off, although the only thing one noticed was the continuous noise of engines and the gleam of the aircraft's navigation lights in the gloom as they hurtled across the roadway, not more than fifty feet above our heads.

At nights in our big dormitory ward, sitting on our beds, we would have long yarns. The company was good and we made many new friends. There were plenty of good-natured scuffles and animated discussions making comparisons between Canada and Great Britain, invariably to the latter's disadvantage. The Canadians pointed out that Great Britain compared to Canada in size was no 'more than a pocket handkerchief... You could put the United Kingdom easily into the Great Lakes'. Our coinage was a silly system with its farthings, half-pennies, pennies, threepenny bits, sixpences and shillings, compared to the Canadian dollar with its one-hundred cents. One of them, Stephens, was particularly derogatory but he was a good fellow notwithstanding and together with a student from McGill University, named Bill Bolt, I enjoyed taking walks. Bill Bolt was not so verbally aggressive

41

and a much more tolerant type — a kind fellow, who unfortunately lost his life some months later when he was appointed to a ship in the Mediterranean, H.M.S. *Sarnia*, which was mined. Another Canadian with whom I became very friendly was a Roman Catholic, called Jones, from La Salle, an amusing fellow who used to recount his amorous adventures in Pompey to our delight in the dormitory at nights, and display triumphantly brassieres, panties and other intimate articles of female underwear which he had captured. I was not to be denied a *soupçon* of romance myself for early in August I was invited to play tennis at Staff Surgeon and Mrs. Connell's in the terrace and here met a most attractive girl of about my own age who was a W.R.N. engaged on servicing coastal motorboats at Fort Brockhunt.

Circumstances were moving and on the 10th August J. S. Lyle was given two hours' notice to repair on board S.S. *Knight Templar* which was sailing shortly for America. However, he arrived back in Haslar next day, having missed his ship and meanwhile no word had come for me about a ship. On 31st August I received my monthly pay amounting to £18 and made the note 'this is really the first time I have had to deal with a large quantity of money. This morning in the operating theatre I gave my 15th anaesthetic... In one of the wards I met a sailor from H.M.S. *Sheldrake*, which is a destroyer in the same flotilla as *Acorn*. He says she is presently at Brindisi.'

* * *

And then on 2nd September I received orders to join H.M.S. *Acorn* in the Mediterranean, making the journey overseas via Cherbourg, Taranto and Malta. There was time to get some hot weather clothing which I bought second-hand from Goldmann's on Portsmouth Hard (a white sola helmet, white cap covers and two suits of white drill).

Armed with travelling warrant when I left Haslar on Sunday, 9th September, I entrained for Southampton and was fortunate in meeting a Warrant Officer who was going in the same draft and was bound for Malta. At Southampton Docks a big American Transport was just docking not far away from our ship, the *Caesarea*, formerly a Channel Island ferry. Hundreds of Americans were disembarking, all of them presenting a novel sight in their freshly ironed uniforms of khaki, their tunics buttoned up to the chin, their legs encased in gaiters or leggings, and on their heads 'boy scout' types of hat in place of the usual caps worn by British troops. They had just arrived from America and were in high spirits and anxious to get to grips with the enemy and, coming after four years of war, were a welcome reinforcement. Another welcome sight coming on board the *Caesarea* was Bill McCartan, a fellow student from my year at Queen's and now a surgeon probationer. He had not been to Haslar or had any preliminary training but had come direct from his home in Castlewellan. Like most of the officers and men proceeding on draft to the Mediterranean I was violently sick that first night crossing the Channel to Cherbourg, which we reached the following morning before breakfast. There the six or seven hundred ratings draft were put in trucks and taken to a rest camp on the outskirts of the town and as officers we were permitted to make our own way thence. Delighted at the prospect of finding myself abroad for the first time I went into a café and asked the smart young waitress there for breakfast or early lunch. There was fish on the menu so I said: 'Mademoiselle, est ce que je pourrai avoir du poison, s'il vous plait?', whereupon the young waitress regarded me with a smile and queried 'Monsieur desire du poison?' When I repeated the request she turned to the other men in the restaurant who were eating there and announced, 'Ce monsieur demande du poison!' Whereupon there were smiles all round and I realised my pronounciation was at fault for quickly correcting it to 'du poisson' the order was immediately complied with. A good breakfast or lunch, with coffee, cost us 3.50 francs each, and from a shop nearby I purchased a bottle of Vin Ordinaire to fortify myself for the journey.

It rained heavily all that day, which we spent at the rest camp, McCartan and I spending that afternoon censoring mail. The next morning early we embarked on the troop train, which was to convey us all the way to Taranto and to take over eight days in so doing. Like the other officers in the draft we were assigned to coaches, four to each compartment so that we slept one on each side and two on the floor. The ratings were accommodated in a long line of standard cattle trucks and the train was nearly half-a-mile long. On our journey we passed through the towns of Caen, Tours, Bourges, Paray-le-Monial. St. Germain du Mont D'Or, until we came to Lyons. The train proceeded at slow speed and we passed through the town of Caen on an elevated track which ran over the street, the sailors or 'matelots', causing great amusement to the townspeople by running up and down on the roofs of their trucks or hanging their legs over the side and waving to them. Inevitably there were numerous delays when the train was moved into sidings to permit other traffic to get by. The officer in command was hard put to it to control the behaviour of the matelots for as soon as the train stopped in the French countryside, even for ten minutes, they were getting out of the trucks and dashing into the fields bordering the line, in which grapes were growing. Then, as the engine gave a shrill whistle to announce that we were getting under way again there was a great rush to regain the train, the men clambering on board as it began to move. Just outside Paray-le-Monial one of them, a young seaman, had a foot badly crushed by the wheel of the train passing over it and there was some delay, whilst at the station, an ambulance was summoned and he was taken to the local hospital. The advantage of these infrequent halts at stations en route was that we could buy food from the buffet. Thus, at Paray-le-Monial we had an omelette and café au lait for six francs and two delicious peaches for a few sous.

At Tours I struck up an acquaintance with two young French military officers who were on their way to the front. One of them, a cadet, was from St. Cyr. At 9 p.m. on the third evening we arrived at a village where there was a rest camp, in which we passed the night. This was St. Germain du Mont D'Or which lay about two or three miles from the Rhône in a perfect setting of vineyards, the village itself having very narrow, cobbled streets surrounding a square in which there was a big drinking trough which appeared to be used by the village women for washing their clothes. At 7 a.m. the village was practically deserted and except for a cock crowing or a dog barking in the distance there was complete silence. Breakfast was served at the rest camp shortly afterwards, and after a short journey running parallel to the river we rumbled into the great station at Lyons. From thence we passed through mountainous country of extreme grandeur and many long tunnels. Two villages en route — St. Rambert en Bougey and Tenay particularly took my fancy. Then we passed along the shores of Le Lac de Bourget until Aix-les-Bains was reached. There, on the station platform stood a typical Monsieur le Curé, in his black cassock and shovel hat, smiling benevolently and waving his stick at us as the train went by. We were passing through the Savoy Alps by then, and had a clear view of Le Diable à trois Pieds, which was bathed in bright moonlight. And so into the Mont Cenis tunnel.

The next day McCartan and I awoke after it had been our turn to occupy the cushioned seats in the compartment to find ourselves covered by itchy skin and bites which raised big pimples on our hands and face, and indeed over all exposed parts. Another officer travelling with us in the compartment recognised them as bed bug bites and, advising us to pull out the cushions, we uncovered some forty or fifty of the creatures which tried to take cover from the light. I well remember the sickly stench there was as we squashed them and the crack as their shells burst. The Lieutenant R.N.R. with us advised us to amuse ourselves that morning by getting them to race each other on an improvised track on the carriage floor until we grew tired of the sport.

The train was now running through Northern Italy which was not so different to Southern France except that in place of vineyards and wheat we saw mostly Indian corn or maize growing in the fields. We passed through Turin and Asti, Alexandria, Bologna, Rimini, until the train was running along the shore of the Adriatic.

Early on the sixth day, whilst it was still dark and our train standing in a station, it being my turn to occupy one of the seats, I saw someone inserting the handle of a walking stick through the half-open window of the carriage and trying to hook a pair of binoculars off the luggage rack, which he then tried to draw through the window. The stick was instantly withdrawn when I awoke and gave a shout but on opening the carriage door and looking along the platform there was no trace of the intruder.

We stopped for a third time at the rest camp at Faenza which was very well organised, baths and a proper meal being provided for all hands. Before and after lunch an orchestra played selections from the grand operas. The journey along the Adriatic was very hot, vegetation being sparse and olive trees predominating in the landscape. At ten o'clock in the morning we stopped at Castellamare and had a bathe off the sandy beach, which was most refreshing. Other places we passed through before coming to our destination at Taranto were Foggia and Bari. By then the only plant life to be seen were cactus, prickly pear, olive and fig trees, the earth having a ploughed-up appearance and bearing no grass whatever, the sky still remaining cloudless.

On arrival at Taranto on the eighth day we changed into whites and were billeted in a huge camp of Nissen huts where I remained for nearly a week in idleness, reporting to the naval transport officer each day about the possibility of a ship going to Malta, and the rest of the time spent yarning with other naval officers on passage. One of these was a hydrophone expert who entertained us by reproducing on his violin the different sounds and rhythms made by ships' engines transmitted under water — the sound of a tramp steamer's single screw driven by a steam reciprocating engine; the sound of Diesel motors as from a submarine; the note produced by a destroyer's engines running at full speed, and a cruiser. This officer had made a very thorough study of the subject and indeed possessed almost uncanny powers of interpretation of the different sounds.

McCartan went on his way a few days later to take passage for Malta and join his ship, H.M.S. *Pentstemon*. Another Queensman, surgeon probationer T. H. Crozier in my year, joined the camp shortly afterwards, the two of us spending our few days rest together watching the Italian Fleet moving in and out of the locks guarding the inner harbour and enabling them to exercise in the basin of the harbour, and visiting the Naval Officers' Club which was a lovely building of stone, with great patios and sheltered loggias, where we could imbibe ice-cooled drinks of vermouth and take little dishes of Italian ice-cream flavoured with mint, but quite different from the British counterpart because these had both the consistency and colour of water. In the evenings at the rest camp there was an outdoor cinema show and in the huts numerous showerbaths but although I seemed to spend hours standing under them they had no effect in making me feel cooler, which was not surprising as the outdoor temperature under the cloudless sky was seldom less than 100°F.

1. I learned that this custom had been established in the eighteenth century, officers in the Navy remaining seated during the drinking of the Royal Toast because of the lack of headroom between decks in the old wooden ships.

2. Dr. Hildred Carlill was a physician on the staff of the Westminster Hospital and a neurologist and colleague of Sir James Purves Stewart, who became famous for his classical book *Diagnosis of Nervous Diseases*, in which Carlill contributed many illustrations. Carlill was an excellent teacher.

3. Admiralty Fleet Order.

Personal Recollections of Experiences in the Mediterranean in the Closing Phase of the War

I remember the tremendous feeling of elation that gripped me on the 18th September when at last, having travelled by train to Brindisi I found the port in a state of blackout on account of air raids. I boarded the duty picket boat and was conveyed across the harbour to H.M.S. *Acorn*, which lay there with other destroyers at anchor. She was due to proceed to sea on patrol the next morning at 0800 hours. Mounting the accommodation ladder, saluting the quarter-deck and the officer of the day, a tall, bearded sub-lieutenant, R.N.V.R., named J. H. R. Giles, I was ushered down the companion way into the wardroom. There, in spite of the blackout screen on the door, it was not unpleasantly hot — an electric fan attached to the deckhead creating some circulation of air. I was presented to the captain — Commander William B. Mackenzie, R.N., and the First Lieutenant, Lieutenant Donald K. Bain, R.N., a young man of about twenty-one; a sub-lieutenant R.N., called R. P. Wilkinson, who was shortly to be relieved; the warrant gunner, Mr. H. J. Perryer and the artificer engineer officer, Mr. Benjamin S. Killock. Shortly afterwards the captain and first lieutenant went ashore, Giles remaining as duty officer, and he drummed up the pantry so that soon I was settled with a tankard of beer and a plate of sandwiches. He explained that no cabin was available for me and that, like my predecessor, I should have the choice of slinging a hammock in the alleyway or sleeping in the wardroom, an ordinary seaman named Chapman being told off for looking after my bedding and clothes, which were stored in drawers beneath the settees, which occupied the sides of the wardroom. For washing and shaving I should have to rely on the other officers' courtesy but Mr. Perryer assured me there would be no difficulty and that I could even arrange to use the tin bath once or twice a week like the other officers.

The next morning I was up at 7 o'clock and, standing on deck beneath the oilskin canopy surrounding the wardroom hatch, I watched the ship, in company with three other destroyers — *Goshawk*, *Ruby* and *Chameleon*, proceeding to sea on patrol past a number of Italian warships, part of the crew being drawn up on the fo'c'sle, as is customary on entering and leaving harbour. The bosun's pipe sounded the still as we passed the foreign warships, and the colours were dipped. The patrol took us between the Italian coast, at Brindisi, across the Adriatic to the enemy-occupied Dalmatian Coast, our course being interrupted at intervals to take on a zigzag pattern and our speed being at 12-15 knots. In addition, at periodic intervals we stopped, the ship being allowed to drift, with the engines and all sounds cut off, in order that the hydrophone ratings on the bridge could listen in for any extraneous sounds and especially the notes given out by a submarine's diesel engines. By day we scarcely noticed these pauses except when there was a seaway and the ship rolled abominably, but at night I used to waken and listen to the gurgling of water in the bilges and the eerie silence that prevailed for the few minutes before the regular beat of the engines was resumed and we proceeded on our allotted patrol. Incidentally, I found it of great help at night to wear my half-inflated Gieve's waistcoat because it gave support and prevented a sudden, unexpected roll throwing one to the deck.

The other officers, who were not on watch-keeping duty, had cabins of their own but the captain who, of course, was not a regular watchkeeper and slept either in his own cabin in the wardroom flat or forward in the charthouse under the bridge used to visit the wardroom at night and if I happened to be awake would stop and chat for a moment and pull my leg about the easy life I had, not having to keep watch at night like the others. Donald Bain,[1] the first lieutenant, was an efficient officer and kept a firm hand on the ship's company but he could be most irascible and moody at times, especially at breakfast when he would complain that he felt 'liverish' and acted like a spoiled child, shouting and abusing the Maltese stewards because his egg was too hardboiled or too soft for his liking. Perryer and the engineer officer took their meals in silence and said little. Among the ship's company I liked best the coxswain or senior non-commissioned rating, a leading seaman called Tozer. He taught me the ropes, taking me all over the ship and explaining the different messes, i.e. the seamen's, stokers' and petty officers'. He also indoctrinated me into the ritual of venereal disease prevention, and the positioning of first aid bags about the ship: on deck; beside the guns and torpedo tubes; in the engine room, and on the bridge.

The prophylactics in use in 1918 against venereal disease were known as 'dreadnoughts' and consisted of tubes of mercury ointment for smearing over the glans penis, preparatory to sexual intercourse, and other tubes containing an antiseptic, the contents of which were to be squeezed into the urethra after coitus. Every sailor going ashore was expected to approach the coxswain and arm himself with such in case he contracted a dose of syphilis or gonorrhoea. Failure to report or concealing the disease laid a man open to punishment by having his leave stopped or more drastic measures. In point of fact, however, important as it was to take some precautions against infection, the drugs then prescribed were more or less useless in averting venereal disease, which was not brought under control until the issue of rubber condoms or French letters became obligatory in all ships, these being obtained on demand and without charge.

We made two more patrols between the 18th September and the 30th of the month, these following the same routine, and except that we encountered bad weather on the second patrol, were without event. However, the officers and crew were kept on the alert notwithstanding because, as already mentioned, earlier in that same year, 1918, the Austrians had suddenly launched an attack on the barrage one night when they had sunk a number of drifters by gunfire, damaged the destroyer H.M.S. *Hornet*, and sunk H.M.S. *Phoenix*.

When our ship was not at sea on patrol we secured at the 'trot', alongside which destroyers of the flotilla moored on either side, and one was free to go ashore and visit the town and its surroundings. I remember on one occasion, taking a walk with Bearblock, the surgeon probationer of *Goshawk*, going through some vineyards adjoining the harbour area when we ate freely of the grapes which were growing on the ground and which only later we discovered were manured with human excreta. In fact, there was a Fleet Order posted in the ship warning all naval personnel against eating grapes because of the dangers of dysentery.

But to revert to the ship, my medicine chest, a bulky object, had been stored in the starboard battery room, which was a small compartment about 4 feet x 3 feet, and which Tozer suggested could be converted for use into a sick bay. This sounded reasonable but when I approached the first lieutenant he resisted the idea, saying that the space was valuable and could not be spared for such a purpose. However, in the ensuing month I persisted with my request and finally gained the captain's permission to have the space turned into a sick bay. Here I could attend every morning at 9 o'clock and sit for 15-20 minutes waiting for any sick ratings to turn up. There was too little room to accommodate two people comfortably, but the ratings would place a foot on the coaming of the compartment and speak to me through the open door. The coxswain provided me with a number of navigating officer's notebooks, in which a list of the cases and their symptoms could be kept.

* * *

About the 25th September, when I had been a little more than a week in the ship, the base was overwhelmed by the current influenza epidemic which was sweeping Europe at the time and taking a heavy toll of life in the principal cities, such as Rome, Paris and London. On board *Acorn*, as in many other ships, the epidemic struck suddenly. One day when we were at sea on patrol I received a message from the bridge that the captain was feeling unwell and that the duty signalman also felt ill and was complaining of pain on breathing and vertiginous sensations. I found the latter with a high temperature. There were no physical signs but I put him off duty and advised him to turn in to his hammock. Within the next three hours six more seamen and stokers were affected in the same way and I advised the captain that we would be wise to return to port and break off the patrol. That evening a dozen more of the crew were similarly taken ill and confined to their hammocks, and I made a signal to the P.M.O. in H.M.S. *Blenheim*, our depot ship, for assistance. By the next morning Sub. Lieutenant Giles, R.N.V.R. and myself were the only officers still fit for duty and of the crew there were insufficient hands to work the ship, only three E.R.As, two stokers, and two officers remaining well. The remainder all had a fever, persistent headache, were unfit for duty and confined to their hammocks. I spent that day crawling around the sick beneath the hammocks, and giving them each ten grains of Dover's powder in a hot drink. Then, after a surgeon lieutenant and an S.B.A. from the *Blenheim* came on board and confirmed that there was an epidemic of influenza, I was recommended to prescribe a diaphoretic mixture, a gallon of which was brought on board by the S.B.A. for doling out to the sick. The following morning all the affected officers and men were taken ashore to hospital, the most seriously ill being placed in cots or Neill-Robertson stretchers and hoisted over the side into a lighter by means of a block and tackle. By that time five of my patients were delirious, their breathing was rapid and they appeared to be suffering from pneumonia. I learned later that two of them subsequently died in hospital. The ship was then disinfected, sulphur candles being burned on the messdecks and in the wardroom flat and engine room, we, the few unaffected by influenza, making out the best we could.

It was now approaching the end of the month and we learned that on the 3rd October the combined British and Italian fleets at Brindisi, together with the Air Force, were to mount an attack on the enemy-held Albanian coast, at the fortified town of Durazzo. For this purpose the ship's company of H.M.S. *Beaver*, another destroyer of the same flotilla, which had not been affected by influenza, was put on board *Acorn*, together with the few unaffected members of the original ship's company crew. Giles, the sub-lieutenant welcomed this chance of action. He had already fought at Zeebrugge and pointed out that I should consider myself lucky because there were still many officers serving in the Navy after four years of war who had 'never even heard a gun fired in anger'. How true this was I did not know but the night before the attack I spent in the wardroom with the other officers of *Beaver* practising the use of tourniquets and bandaging, my shipmates readily volunteering themselves as models. Next morning I awoke early, shortly after six o'clock, to find a party of ratings in the wardroom. They had lifted the two manhole covers in the deck and were passing up four-inch and twelve-pounder ammunition from the magazine for use at the guns. Later that morning, as we prepared for sea, I took over the seamen's messdeck forrad and arranged for splints, drugs and dressings to be placed on messtables there with a large bowl of 1 in 20 carbolic, towels and bandages. The wardroom was also cleared and drugs and dressings left there provisionally. I was wearing a clean white drill suit like the other officers and had a syringe with morphine attached to my jacket pocket, the morphine being contained in a small rubber-capped sterile bottle. During the succeeding action, which took us across the Adriatic to within a few miles of the Albanian coast and Durazzo, morphine was the only drug required. The ship was not hit and we sustained no casualties except that the quarter-master, who was steering the ship from beneath the bridge, had to be relieved of his duties as he became acutely hysterical. We were in the van of the attack, *Acorn, Shark* and *Goshawk* acting as minesweepers for the heavy Italian cruisers, the *San Georgio* and *San Marco*, and I promptly gave the man a hypodermic injection of one-third gram of morphine and had him relieved, after which he became quiet and gave no further trouble. One of our light cruisers, H.M.S. *Weymouth*, was hit by a torpedo in the stern and had to leave the line, being brought back under tow by destroyers to Brindisi. The action was short, lasting no more than an hour-and-a-half and I felt awed by the sound of the heavy guns from the shore batteries and the shells screaming through the air towards and around us. One I saw plunging into the sea and just missing an Italian torpedo boat, a column of water and spray being thrown up virtually alongside it.

After the action we were sent for a refit and boiler clean to the dockyard at Genoa, where we remained (most of the time in dry dock) for a fortnight or so before being directed to rejoin the fleet which, on the 11th November, Armistice Day, had steamed up the Dardanelles to Constantinople, as it was then called, the destroyers being based nearby in the Gulf of Ismid, which made a good anchorage and was about the same size as Scapa Flow. Along its perimeter was farmland and the railway line running to Baghdad passed along it.

In Genoa, free shore leave was granted and I and another surgeon probationer called James Kerr of the Clyde Division took the opportunity of going up to Milan, staying two nights there in an hotel, seeing the famous Duomo (Cathedral) with its remarkable statue of the saint who had been skinned alive and whose musculature was exposed. It was evident that the sculptor had a very excellent knowledge of the anatomy of the human body.

The next day we spent on Lake Como, four of us making up a party with myself, Kerr and two Australian military officers, and we went on the lake steamer from one end to the other, seeing many very beautiful villages en route. On leaving Genoa at the end of the refit we called at Spezia, the Italian naval base, to refuel with oil and thence our voyage to Malta was taken between the coasts of Italy, Corsica and Sardinia, the ship being blacked out and zigzagging as usual, but nothing untoward happened although on the Eve of the Armistice we received a signal that H.M.S. *Brittania*, an old pre-Dreadnought type of battleship, had been torpedoed in the Straits of Gibraltar.

We arrived in Malta, (it was my first visit to the island) on the morning of the 11th November, steaming into the entrance under Fort St. Elmo to the accompaniment of the church bells of Valetta, which were pealing joyfully in honour of the official beginning of peace. Having secured to buoys in Dockyard Creek, shore leave was granted to officers and men, and one of the first persons I met that day in Valetta was Arthur Eaton, like myself a surgeon probationer and in my own year at Queen's. We had a wonderful time doing sightseeing in Valetta, in particular visiting the ancient church which was celebrated for the dryness of its atmosphere. The altar was formed of human bones, all in an excellent state of preservation. Arthur Eaton and I celebrated our reunion by dining together at the Great Britain Hotel in the Strada Reale, and imbibing more wine than we should have done. But we had a great deal to talk about and his experiences in the sloop H.M.S. *Honeysuckle* did not seem to have been any less varied than had mine.

Two days later we sailed for Constantinople, taking Captain Basil Fanshawe as passenger, and an amusing episode occurring as the ship was preparing for sea and leaving the Grand Harbour. The captain had been a little worried by the loss of his First Lieutenant to hospital. That day No. 1 had developed an enormous boil on the most tender part of his anatomy, and I had unsuccessfully attempted to lance it on the passage down from Genoa. At any rate, the captain was a little confused in his mind and seemed not fully to comprehend that we were in the Mediterranean. He came on deck wearing an oilskin and a Sou'wester with sea boots, as if he were about to enter the North Sea. Striding forward along the main deck he saw a stoker who had unwisely poised himself in an open manhole in the deck. This proved an irresistible target for him. Uttering an oath, he tried to plant his heavily-booted foot on the head of the unfortunate man. Later that evening, whilst on the bridge and descending the ladder from it to the fo'c'sle, he fell and all but dislocated his shoulder so that I was called to his assistance. In place of the First Lieutenant we had a Sub-Lieutenant R.N. named Willis, who acted as navigator and was first class at his task. Poor Willis suffered from seasickness but never once gave in nor went off duty because of it, and we became close friends. It was hinted that his father or some other close relative was a very high ranking officer but we never discussed the matter. Our voyage from Malta took us past Cape Matapan in the Aegean and thençe past the Island of Samothrace and Imbros near to the entrance to the Dardanelles, across the Sea of Marmara to Constantinople and finally to our anchorage at Ismid.

* * *

Ismid always had a peculiar nostalgic effect on me. Often we would take the dinghy and go ashore in the surrounding countryside, calling on farmers and bartering cigarettes or such like goods for chickens or even vegetables. Twice we raised a Rugby team from the flotilla and played a match against the officers of *Temerere*. I played in the game and remember that on our side was a Lieut. Crutchley, V.C. of Zeebrugge fame. About twice a week it was our turn to make the duty trip to Constantinople and there we would lie alongside the Galatea Bridge for an hour or two before returning. On one occasion an elderly surgeon commander took Willis and me on a visit to the Mosque of San Sophia, which only recently had been returned to its proper use, for many years having been used as a stable for horses of the Turkish cavalry. I remember the Fleet Surgeon bartering with the Turks in the underground bazaar for carpets and the amazing effect it had on them when he produced a £1 note and explained the illustration on the back showing the House of Commons at Westminster. It was apparent then that British currency was much sought after and considered by other nationals to be of great value. At that time Turkey was being deluged by out-dated Russian roubles. Later, in a shop in Sevastapol I was able to acquire some 300 roubles for a second-hand pair of shoes. A snotty in the *Temerere* went one better by bartering his motor-bicycle for a fabulous sum of roubles, but unfortunately the deal fell through when it was found the paper notes were worthless.

It was not an infrequent occurrence when walking about the streets of Istanbul to encounter numbers of sailors from the battle cruiser *Goeben*, which was lying since the Armistice in the anchorage at Ismid. One imagined that there would be trouble over these fortuitous meetings, but on the contrary, the Germans invariably stepped aside off the sidewalk and saluted us as they passed.

On six occasions the *Acorn* took on the duty of mail and despatch boat between Constantinople and Sevastapol, the journey occupying about twenty-four hours, dependent on the weather which was often very bad. On another occasion when we entered the Black Sea it was in company with an old French cruiser, the *Jules Michelet*, and the destroyer, H.M.S. *Brisk*, our object being to 'show the flag' and enforce the terms of the Armistice in Turkey. Cruising along the southern shore of the Black Sea we called at remote places, i.e. Sinope, Samsun and Trebizond, on each occasion the captain going ashore and presenting his credentials to the Turkish governor. Language was often a difficulty, none of our officers having any French or German, and on some occasions I was taken along as interpreter. One night there was great excitement on shore because of full scale rioting by the Turks against the Armenians, and Giles arranged for a landing party to be put ashore, if necessary. I was issued with field rations and a service revolver, Giles encouraging me to practise with the gun on the quarter deck. Fortunately, our assistance was not required and apart from the sounds of shooting ashore the night passed without event.

We made at least four trips to Sevastapol and Giles and the captain and I arranged to make a tour of the old Crimean battlefield of Balaclava. The town itself was certainly very disturbed with the population mostly keeping indoors and shops closed, a fearful apprehension gripping them. We lay in the dockyard within easy proximity to the town, the houses overlooking the ships. At night there was occasional sniping and it was very cold with the temperature below zero, although, now the proud occupant of Donald Bain's vacant cabin, I was most comfortable. One evening the services of a landing party were again called for, this time to give support to a detachment of Royal Marines who were occupying the town station and guarding an ammunition train, the possession of which was under dispute between the 'Red' and 'White' Russian forces. I shall never forget the sight of that station with some three or four hundred Russian peasants and their families waiting for a train to take them out of the beleagured city. They lay sleeping across the tracks in the freezing cold with little hope of escape, as most of the rolling stock was out of action.

On another occasion, again at Sevastapol, when the captain had gone ashore with Giles, and Willis and I were the only officers left in the ship, a commotion began on board a large Russian yacht lying alongside *Acorn* — it may have been an ex-Royal yacht. At any rate, Willis and I were both frightened, but we went on board the yacht, each of us armed and with a sailor accompanying us, and made a thorough search. Everywhere there was destruction, smashed mirrors, broken chairs and excreta defiling the walls. When we penetrated down to the main deck we found a fire smouldering amid rubbish in one of the cabins but this was quickly extinguished, and there was no further disturbance.

On Christmas Day, 1918, we lay alongside a cruiser, H.M.S. *Foresight*, and close to the battleship *Temerere*, and there was great jollification. In *Acorn*, as customary, a seaman was selected as captain. He wore the Captain's brass hat and uniform jacket as he marched about the deck accompanied by a party of other seamen, pretending to make an inspection. Afterwards, the officers made a round of the mess-decks and the rum flowed freely. This was followed by Christmas dinner, although I cannot remember whether this included turkey or goose. That evening at about midnight, we slipped out of Sevastapol and proceeded along the coast to Yalta to come to the aid of a beleagured Grand Duke and his wife — the Grand Duke Alexander and the Duchess, who came down to the quayside at about 0700 in a typical Russian-style drosky and were taken on board, together with their *aide-de-camp*, a young Russian officer known as Prince Olaf. The journey back to Sevastapol only took about two hours and during this time I had the privilege of rendering first aid to the Grand Duchess who was very seasick, and had difficulty in managing to operate the vacuum pump in the heads. At Sevastapol we turned the Royal party over to the captain of *Foresight* and they were taken thence to Malta.[2] Prince Olaf told us that less than a week before some ten or twenty officers of the old Imperial Forces had been lined up on the wall of the breakwater at Yalta and shot out of hand by machinegun fire. By contrast, our Commander-in-Chief, with a view to suppressing the unrest in the town, hanged six malcontents from the yardarm of H.M.S. *Temerere*.

Later, we made a trip from Sevastapol to Novorrisk on the far side of the Black Sea, the object being to land two officials or agents of the British Foreign Office, but in February we were detailed away from Russia to minesweeping duties in and about the approaches to the Dardanelles. Several live mines were brought to the surface by paravane and destroyed by rifle fire and there were some exciting moments when live mines drifted past the ship, almost within touching distance. Two or three merchant ships, Greek or Turkish owned, wandered out of the swept channels, when a warning had to be conveyed to them that they were standing in danger by a shot fired across their bows.

We made several excursions ashore at the Dardanelles to the site of the former battlefields, which then had not been disturbed, and one came across many grisly sights such as a half-clothed skeleton caught in barbed wire, bits of uniform and torn decomposed flesh from the explosion of a grenade. One of our sailors, who had been granted shore leave put up a black by bringing back to the ship a human skull. But when the crew discovered this they became very wrath, accusing the man of bringing bad luck on the ship, and a small deputation of sailors waited on the captain to secure the offending object's removal.

Late in February our ship hoisted a paying-off pennant and set out for the journey home and in due course I was demobilised. On the way we stopped two nights at Malta and I met Eaton again, the two of us attending the great fancy dress ball held in connection with the Malta Carnival celebrations. At Gibraltar we made a second stop and met many of the destroyers en route for Malta to relieve us. Crossing the Bay we encountered bad weather, with heavy seas and since Bain had rejoined the ship at Malta, I found temporary cabin accommodation in the extreme after end of the ship in the tiller flat, which was a noisy place, being directly over the screws, and poorly ventilated as the manhole had to be closed because the compartment was liable to be flooded by seas if the cover was left open.

On arrival at Devonport the ship was moored in Salthouse Creek, and proceeding to the Naval Barracks I was issued with my demobilisation papers and some back pay before being released from the service. I recommenced my studies at Queen's in time for the following summer term.

1. Rose to be a Captain, R.N. and in the Second World War commanded *Norfolk* during the pursuit and destruction of *Bismarck*.

2. I thought this was the end of the matter, but by a curious coincidence, one evening when visiting a friend's house in London I met the wife of another doctor, a Russian lady, who turned out to be the daughter of the Grand Duchess, and learned that her parents had after their rescue settled in Paris where they had taken up residence and opened a highly successful restaurant. Afterwards, when I sent her a photograph of her parents, standing on the quarter deck of *Acorn* with their little terrier dog beside them, and the ship leaving Yalta, she assured me that although at the time she was still unborn and invisible, she, too, had been in the photograph!

Envoy

In this account of the surgeon probationers one has been very aware of lack of detail and incompleteness. After the lapse of so many years and the slender evidence of their activities still extant, it has not been easy. But I hope to have shown that this Admiralty-directed experiment in using medical students in time of war was successful. Unlike their predecessors, the surgeon's mates, rarely did they abuse their privileges and responsibilities, and some actually gained official recognition for their gallantry and devotion to duty.

The chief reasons for writing about them have been: first, as a token of respect to their memory. Medically speaking they may have achieved little more than the modern sick berth attendant could have done, and during the Second World War, in fact, did achieve. But in those earlier days in small craft where the surgeon probationers filled the gap satisfactorily and by their presence received the courtesy title of 'doctor', they gave the sailors that measure of confidence which has ever been shown to be essential in battle. Vice Admiral R. J. Willan has written: 'So many destroyer captains averred that surgeon probationers were of great assistance, particularly in the small fighting units... Their presence in action gave confidence to the ship's company.'

On the whole, in the course of their duty in medical day-to-day charge they had little to do. But they willingly undertook non-medical duties, such as decoding, assisting in the correction of charts in response to A.F.O.s, in keeping the wine books; and in censoring the mail. I believe that when he left his ship, one irresponsible young surgeon probationer received a 'flimsy' from his captain stating only that he 'had served in the ship for six months, kept the wine books, and played the gramophone in the wardroom rather well!' To counter this impression I have discovered that another young probationer, Christopher Howard Andrewes,[1] a medical student from St. Bartholomew's in 1918, who served in the sloop H.M.S. *Marigold* at the end of the war, kept a daily diary in which he recorded current war news, any medical cases that occurred, but was chiefly concerned with ornithological and entomological detail which he compiled, because he spent much of his free time exploring the surrounding countryside and logging his experiences.

In the Second World War the navy did not take medical students but this was because conditions had changed. There was a sufficiency of qualified doctors and the authorities took the view that all medical students should be exempted from naval and military service and allowed to continue their studies without interruption until they had graduated. There may have been overwhelming arguments in favour of this policy at the time but not one of the former surgeon probationers would deny that their employment at the impressionable age of nineteen or twenty gave them a new slant on their profession, an attitude of mind that could not have been acquired if they had remained in civilian life. Their period in the navy broadened their outlook and, although in their day little attention was paid to psychological aspects of medicine, it provided them with practical day-to-day experience of human behaviour and helped to bridge this important gap in their training curriculum.

The threat of a new world war seems remote, but in its place there is the world-wide tendency to civilian revolt against authority and disillusionment in ideals in general. The navy, however, remains as important as it ever was, especially in preserving a sufficiency of small ships to ensure the population's survival in wartime by the safe conduct of foodstuffs and munitions.

In medical schools throughout the country the importance of psychological medicine has now been recognised. As part of their training medical students are advised to spend part of their time under the aegis of well-established practitioners, to make home visits with them, to deal with relatively trivial complaints whilst still having their principals to fall back upon in case of difficulty. This system has met with success and entails no burden on public expenditure. One would hope, indeed, that the tendency should grow and that medical students might be seconded to work full-time with medical practitioners, as they were during the great war, for longer, i.e. 6-9 months. The effect of such a break in their study could be helpful. One might even go so far as to suggest that the Admiralty might extend the present system of receiving only a limited number of medical students as sub-lieutenants to each division of the R.N.R. to increase the number and provide facilities for them to serve in small sea-going ships, living with the ship's companies, receiving pay, and being responsible for their day-to-day medical care for short periods of 3-6 months. Under the present system reserve medical officers are only required to spend 14-30 days 'training' each year. By modifying this arrangement, not only could the medical student's horizons be increased, but it could provide a stronger reserve for the navy which would assure their allegiance to the service much more than does the panoply of uniform and familiarity with regulations and naval routine and customs.

1. Later, he acquired a knighthood and an F.R.S. and became a Fellow of the Royal College of Physicians, and the Oliver Sharpey Lecturer in 1934. At the National Institute of Medical Research he became Director and famous for his authorship of *Viruses of Vertebrates* and *The Natural History of the Common Cold.*

Part II

CLINICAL NOTES

FOR

SURGEON PROBATIONERS, R.N.V.R.,

BY

R. J. WILLAN,

M.V.O.: M.S. DURHAM: F.R.C.S. ENGLAND: STAFF SURGEON, R.N.V.R,
HONORARY ~~ASSISTANT~~ SURGEON AND LECTURER OF CLINICAL SURGERY
TO THE ROYAL VICTORIA INFIRMARY, NEWCASTLE-UPON-TYNE.
DEMONSTRATOR OF SURGICAL PATHOLOGY TO THE DURHAM UNIVERSITY
COLLEGE OF MEDICINE,

Title page from R. J. Willan's book.

(Note:- *The page numbers of the original text are shown in brackets in italics, so that readers may follow the cross references and index.*)

(page 2)

PREFACE

This book owes its origin to a series of clinical lectures and demonstrations, which I was asked to give to Surgeon Probationers in the Royal Naval Hospital Ship "Plassy," at a Naval Base. My endeavour aimed at the student acquiring some practical well digested information, rather than have him go away with an undigested medley of knowledge which would be of little use to him as a Surgeon Probationer. The diseases dealt with are the ones they are ordinarily liable to meet *in a man of Naval Rating age* (*i.e.*, between 16 and 38) upon ships of a size which carry a Surgeon Probationer. Part I. deals with acute abdominal emergencies, while some other ailments are referred to in Part II.

A "typical" case is one where the disease follows a certain course and presents definite symptoms and signs; an "atypical" case is one which fails to follow the normal course, when one or more of the ordinary symptoms or signs may be absent or replaced by others. I have only dealt with typical cases, but remember that there are exceptions to every rule, only that the exceptions are uncommon. Also remember that these Notes are purposely incomplete, for only the main features are mentioned; if they were complete, they would be too voluminous to be useful. They are intended as "Guide Posts" only for a Surgeon Probationer of limited experience. As the junior student gathers knowledge he must make the necessary additions for himself.

When examining a case, the student should give himself every chance by only making an examination under the best possible conditions; *e.g.*, a good light and a full view. Wherever there is a chance of

(page 3)
comparing the normal with the abnormal, always do so; *e.g.*, in a case of knee-joint trouble, fully expose both knees and compare the normal with the diseased one. It is quite true that there may be no facilities in his ship for examining urine, staining microscopic slides, &c.; some are as yet unskilled with a stethoscope; some cannot yet estimate any alteration in the "vocal fremitus"; yet even the junior hospital student can

63

make out a great deal, if he will only try, without such aids or knowledge. It is a well-known fact that in "doctoring" the mistakes are usually *not* made through lack of knowledge, but through a failure to adequately examine the patient.

The Surgeon Probationer should always endeavour to obtain the services of a Surgeon in any case of sickness. In civil life the successful Practitioner is the one who does not consider it an indignity to have a second opinion about a case. If the Surgeon Probationer is really interested in his work, he will make it a point of honour to thoroughly learn all the symptoms and signs of his case, also to arrive at some diagnosis. At the consultation with the Surgeon he will have his various points confirmed or refuted, and he is so much the richer for knowledge which he will have acquired.

It must be emphasised that the prescriptions, &c. given are only to be used when a Surgeon is not available for a consultation.

A (49)2286*a* Wt 51389—P 133 400 5/17 E & S A 2

Clinical Notes For Surgeon Probationers: (Part I)

(*page* 5)

PART I:
ACUTE ABDOMINAL DISEASES LIKELY TO
BE MET WITH IN A PERSON OF
NAVAL RATING AGE:

1. WHERE THERE IS NO HISTORY OF AN INJURY, THINK OF:—
   ACUTE APPENDICITIS.
   RUPTURED GASTRIC OR DUODENAL ULCER.
   ACUTE PERITONITIS *e.g.* ACUTE TUBERCULOSIS.
   ACUTE GASTRITIS.
   ACUTE INTESTINAL OBSTRUCTION.
   RENAL CALCULUS.
   ACUTE INTESTINAL COLIC.
      But beware of:—
         ACUTE PNEUMONIA.
         ACUTE PLEURISY.
         ACUTE DILATATION OF THE HEART.
         ACUTE PYELITIS.
         ACUTE EPIDIDYMITIS.
         TABES DORSALIS.
         ACUTE INFECTIOUS FEVERS.
2. WHERE THERE IS A HISTORY OF INJURY, THINK OF:—
   INTERNAL BLEEDING.
   RUPTURED BLADDER.
   FRACTURED RIBS.

(*page* 6)

THE CLINICAL INVESTIGATION OF AN
ACUTE ABDOMINAL CASE OF
NAVAL RATING AGE.

Always first look at the patient and decide in your own mind if he is ill or if he is not.

THE SYMPTOMS:—
[*i.e.*, the HISTORY of the case.]
    The ONSET:—
        (1) As acute pain, vomiting, rigor, or shock.
        (2) If an accident, what happened exactly.
    PAIN (*see* page 42):—
        (1) Its situation — at onset and afterwards.
        (2) If continuous or spasmodic.
        (3) Its relation to food.
        (4) If made worse on deep inspiration.
    VOMITING (*see* pages 43 and 45):—
    Its character and force.
    BOWELS and PASSAGE of FLATUS (*see* page 34):—
        (1) When were the bowels moved last.
        (2) When was flatus passed last.
        (3) The rectal questions refer to —
            (1) Pain.
            (2) Prolapse.
            (3) Discharge.
            (4) Defaecation.

(*page* 7)
    MICTURITION (*see* page 37):—
    The urinary questions refer to:—
        (1) Frequency of micturition.
        (2) Pain, in relation to micturition.
        (3) Character of the stream.
        (4) Character of the urine.
Has he any COUGH (*see* page 44).
Has he had any PREVIOUS ILLNESS resembling it.
THE SIGNS:—
    [*i.e.*, Points discovered upon EXAMINING the patient.]
PULSE RATE (*see* page 33).
TEMPERATURE.
TONGUE.
RESPIRATIONS.
URINE.
INSPECTION:—
    (1) Does the belly wall move on respiration.

(2) Is there any peristalsis — visible, audible, or palpable.

PALPATION:—

(1) Are the hernial sites normal (*see* page 51).

(2) Is there any tender area (*see* page 42).

(3) Is there any rigidity of the belly wall.

PERCUSSION:—

(1) Over the tender area.

(2) Of the flanks for free fluid in the peritoneal cavity.

(*page 8*)

HEART APEX BEAT:—

Define its position. The normal position is in the left fourth intercostal space, half an inch internal to the nipple line.

KNEE JERKS:—

Are they present.

TESTES:—

Is the epididymis tender.

RECTUM:—

Examine for anything abnormal.

HEART SOUNDS.

BREATH SOUNDS.

AIDS FOR ARRIVING AT A DIAGNOSIS OF THE
ACUTE ABDOMINAL EMERGENCIES
MENTIONED IN THE LIST ON PAGE 5.

Suggests:—

The ONSET:—

(1) As acute abdominal pain with vomiting   Any of them.

(2) As a rigor   { Pneumonia. / Pleurisy. / Pyelitis.

(*a*)(3) As marked shock   A ruptured viscus.

(*a*) See page 48.

(*page 9*)

PAIN:—

	Suggests:—
(1) Spasmodic pain occurs with	Renal calculus.
	Intestinal colic.
	Intestinal obstruction.
	Appendicitis.
(2) Pain ¼ to 3 hours after food, *i.e.*,	Gastric ulcer.
prior to emergency	Duodenal ulcer.
(3) Pain worse during a deep inspiration	Pneumonia.
	Pleurisy.

VOMITING:—

(1) If previous to the emergency he	Ruptd. gastric ulcer.
vomited blood	Ruptd. duodenal ulcer.
(2) If it is faecal	Intestinal obstruction.

BOWELS AND PASSAGE OF FLATUS:—

(1) If there is constipation	
(2) If rumblings are seen or heard	Intestinal obstruction.
(3) If flatus cannot be voided	

MICTURITION:—

(1) Increased frequency	Renal calculus.
	Pyelitis.
	Appendicitis (pelvic).
(2) Pain:—	
(*a*) at the posterior renal area	Renal calculus.
	Pyelitis.
	Appendicitis (pelvic).
(*b*) in the urethra during micturition	Pyelitis.
	Epididymitis.

(*page 10*)

MICTURITION—*cont.*

	Suggests:—
(3) Character of stream.	
(4) Character of urine:—	
(*a*) if if contains blood	Renal calculus.
(*b*) if there is a deposit of pus	Pyelitis.
	Urethritis.

(c) if very acid in reaction	Pyelitis.
PULSE RATE:—	
	Appendicitis.
	Internal bleeding.
	Ruptured viscus.
(a) *above* 80 beats per minute	Acute peritonitis.
	Acute diltn. of heart.
	Pneumonia.
	Pleurisy.
	Acute gastritis.
	Intestinal obstruction.
(b) *below* 80 beats per minute	Intestinal colic.
	Renal calculus.
	Tabes dorsalis.
TEMPERATURE:—	
	Acute gastritis.
	Appendicitis.
	Acute peritonitis.
	Pneumonia.
If elevated	Pleurisy.
	Syelitis.
	Epididymitis.
	Acute infectious
	fevers.

(page 11)

Suggests:—

TONGUE:—	
If plastered	Fever.
If moist brown	Constipation.
If dry brown	Failing circulation.
If moist red	Pus.
If dry red	Failing assimilation.
RESPIRATIONS:—	
If above 20 per minute	Pneumonia.
	Pleurisy.

URINE:—
   (*a*) if blood is seen in it   Renal calculus.
   (*b*) if you find pus in it   Pyelitis.
                                        Urethritis.

INSPECTION:—

                                        Ruptured viscus.
   (*a*) if there is *general* limitation of   Acute general
        the belly wall respiratory   peritonitis.
        movements   Fractured lower ribs.

                                          Appendicitis.
   (*b*) if there is *local* limitation of the   Renal calculus.
        belly wall respiratory movements   Ruptured bladder.
                                          Pneumonia.
                                        Pleurisy.
   (*c*) if peristalsis is heard or seen   Intestinal obstruction.

(*page 12*)

                                        Suggests:—

PALPATION:—
   (*a*) if there is a tender swelling at a   Strangulated hernia.
        hernial site
   (*b*) if there is a (*e*) tender area at—
        (1) McBurney's point   Appendicitis.
        (2) the epigastrium   Ruptd. gastric ulcer.
        (3) to the right and just above Ruptd. duodenal
            the umbilicus.   ulcer.
        (4) at the posterior renal area   Renal calculus.
                                        Pyelitis.
        (5) at the posterior renal area, also Pyelitis with
            the middle third of the linea   inflamed ureter.
            semilunaris
        (6) over the inguinal canal   Epididymitis.
   (*c*) if there is rigidity—

                                          Appendicitis.
        (1) over the right iliac fossa   Pyelitis.
                                          Pneumonia.
        (2) over both iliac fossae   Double pyelitis.
        (3) over the hypogastrium   Ruptured bladder.

| (4) general rigidity of the belly wall | Ruptured viscus. Acute peritonitis. Fractured lower ribs. |
| (d) if peristaltic movements are felt. | Intestinal obstruction. |

(e) *See* page 42.

(page 13)

PERCUSSION:—   *Suggests:—*
   If there is dullness in the flanks when   Fluid in the peri-
     the patient rolls over.   toneal cavity, *e.g.,*
                                        blood.

POSITION OF THE HEART APEX
   BEAT:—
   If displaced into the left axilla   Dilatation of the
                                   heart
                                   Right-sided pleurisy
                                    with effusion.

KNEE JERKS:—
   If they are absent   Tabes dorsalis.
TESTES:—
   If the whole epididymis is enlarged and
     tender   Epididymitis.
RECTUM.
HEART SOUNDS.
BREATH SOUNDS:—
   (a) if following an accident crepitus is heard   Fractured ribs.
   (b) if friction is heard *without* a history
     of any accident   Pleurisy.

(page 14)

LEADING POINTS IN THE DIAGNOSIS OF SOME
ACUTE ABDOMINAL CONDITIONS
IN THEIR EARLY STAGES.

In each disease mentioned, the "Scheme" (or Routine) upon pages 6 to 8 has been gone through systematically; where any symptom or sign of the scheme is not mentioned at all, this is an indication that they may be present in an atypical case. It will be noticed that the symptoms and signs are separately bracketed off under the headings, "at onset" and "symptoms and signs which are normal."

If general septic peritonitis follows upon a ruptured appendix, and it be not immediately treated, the patient will probably die about three days after the onset of the illness.

Nine out of ten cases of ruptured viscus (*e.g.*, a ruptured gastric or duodenal ulcer), which are operated upon within *twelve hours* of the perforation should recover. After this time has been allowed to elapse, the chances of the patient's recovery lessens with every hour which passes by without the operation being done.

In acute intestinal obstruction the cause must be promptly dealt with by operation, otherwise the outlook is grave.

To give Opium in any form to a patient complaining of acute abdominal pain, is an absolutely criminal procedure on the part of the Doctor unless he has made a diagnosis. It sometimes requires great courage on the part of the medical man to refuse opium to a patient (who knows its virtues, and who is, perhaps, constantly clamouring for relief from his acute pain,) where the cause of the pain has not been ascertained. The opium masks symptoms, and before its comforting effect has passed off the patient may be moribund.

It is not always a safe procedure giving a purgative where acute abdominal pain is complained of; it is sometimes sufficient to cause a rupture of the acutely inflamed distended vermiform appendix.

(*page 15*)
ACUTE APPENDICITIS.

(1) Perhaps there has been a previous attack.
(2) *The Onset:—*
        Acute right iliac fossa Pain, usually preceded by general abdominal pain.
        Vomiting.
        Tenderness in the right iliac fossa.
        Muscular Rigidity over the right iliac fossa.
(3) *Within a few hours:—*
        The Temperature is elevated.
        Possibly there is   Frequency of micturition.

Pain on micturition.
or, Flexion of the right thigh.

(4) *Symptoms and Signs which are normal:—*
Passage of Flatus.
Respirations.
Urine.
Hernial Sites.
No posterior renal area tenderness.
Heart Apex Beat.
Knee Jerks.
Testes.
Rectum.
Heart Sounds.
Breath Sounds.

(5) *The Treatment is:—*
Immediate Operation.

(*page 16*)
RUPTURED GASTRIC OR DUODENAL ULCER.

1. *Before onset of perforation:—*
Epigastric Pain ¼ to 3 hours after food.
Vomiting of fresh blood, or of altered blood (which has the appearance of coffee grounds), *see* page 45.

2. *At Onset:—*
Severe Pain in the upper abdomen.
Marked Shock with fear of impending death.
Vomiting.
Pulse rate, 100 to 140 per minute.
Respiratory Movements of belly wall absent.
General Rigidity of the belly wall.

3. *Within a few hours:—*
Recovery from the shock.
Tenderness of the upper abdomen.
Continuing belly wall rigidity.
Pulse rate 100, and getting quicker.

4. *Symptoms and Signs which are normal:—*
Bowels and Passage of Flatus.

73

Micturition.
Temperature.
Urine.
Hernial Sites.
Heart Apex Beat.
Knee Jerks.
Testes.
Rectum.
Heart Sounds.
Breath Sounds.
5. *The Treatment is:—*
Immediate Operation.

(*page 17*)

ACUTE GENERAL PERITONITIS.

1. *At Onset:—*
Continuous general Pain in the abdomen.
Vomiting.
Respiratory Movements of belly wall lessened.
General Rigidity of the belly wall.
General Tenderness of the belly wall.
2. *Within a few hours:—*
The pain, vomiting, rigidity, and tenderness persist.
Elevation of temperature.
Quickening of pulse rate.
3. *Symptoms and Signs which are normal:—*
Micturition.
Urine.
Hernial Sites.
Heart Apex Beat.
Knee Jerks.
Heart Sounds.
Breath Sounds.
4. *The Treatment:—*
Depends upon the cause; probably an immediate Operation
will be necessary.

ACUTE GASTRITIS.

1. *Before onset:—*
    An indiscretion of diet.
    Other persons may have the same symptoms.
2. *At onset:—*
    Persistent Vomiting.
    Localised epigastric Pain.
    Usually Diarrhoea.
    Furred Tongue.
    Elevated Temperature.
    Epigastric Tenderness.
3. *Symptoms and Signs which are normal:—*
    Passage of Flatus.
    Micturition.
    Pulse Rate.
    Respirations.
    Hernial Sites.
    Heart Apex Beat.
    Knee Jerks.
    Testes.
    Rectum.
    Heart Sounds.
    Breath Sounds.
4. *The Treatment is:—*
    Rest in bed.
    Starvation for 24 hours, to rest the Stomach.
    Give hot boiled water only.

INTESTINAL OBSTRUCTION, from any cause.

1. *Prior to onset there may be:—*
    Obstinate Constipation.
    Loud intestinal Rumblings, relieved by passing flatus.
2. *At onset:—*
    Spasmodic griping abdominal Pain.
    Increased intestinal Peristalsis, visible, audible, or palpable.

Vomiting — forceful and frequent.

Constipation.

Inability to pass Flatus.

Perhaps external evidence of a cause of obstruction, *e.g.*, a strangulated hernia.

3. *Within a few hours:—*

Continuous vomiting, which may become faecal.

Localised distension of the abdomen.

Peristalsis, which is visible, audible, or palpable.

4. *Symptoms and Signs which are normal:—*

Micturition.

Pulse Rate.

Temperature.

Respirations.

Urine.

No Rigidity.

Heart Apex Beat.

Knee Jerks.

Testes.

Heart Sounds.

Breath Sounds.

5. *The Treatment is:—*

Immediate operation.

(*page 20*)

RENAL CALCULUS.

1. *Before onset:—*

Perhaps a history of previous attacks.

2. *At onset:—*

Often there is a Rigor.

Acute spasmodic Pain, beginning at the posterior renal area, radiating round the flank down the course of the ureter and groin into the testis of the same side (*see* page 42).

Vomiting.

Frequent desire to micturate.

Rigidity of flank muscles.

Tenderness at the posterior renal area.

3. *Within a few hours:—*
    Probably Haematuria.
4. *Symptoms and Signs which are normal:—*
    Bowels.
    Passage of Flatus.
    Pulse Rate.
    Temperature.
    Respirations.
    Hernial Sites.
    Heart Apex Beat.
    Knee Jerks.
    Testes.
    Rectum.
    Heart Sounds.
    Breath Sounds.
5. *The Treatment is:—*
    Send him to hospital for investigation.

(*page 21*)

INTESTINAL COLIC.

1. *Before onset:—*
    An indiscretion of diet.
    Other persons may have the same symptoms.
    Possibly due to Lead poisoning (*see* page 57).
2. *At onset:—*
    Acute spasmodic Pain in abdomen.
    Persistent Diarrhoea, or, obstinate Constipation.
    Sometimes vomiting.
    Furred Tongue.
3. *Symptoms and Signs which are normal:—*
    Passage of Flatus.
    Micturition.
    Pulse Rate.
    Temperature.
    Respirations.
    Urine.
    Hernial Sites.
    No Rigidity.

Heart Apex Beat.
Knee Jerks.
Testes.
Rectum.
Heart Sounds.
Breath Sounds.
4. *The Treatment is:—*
   One ounce of castor oil.
   Light diet for a few days.

(page 22)
   ACUTE PNEUMONIA, simulating an acute Abdominal Lesion.

1. *Prior to onset:—*
   He feels unwell for a few days.
   He may have a Cough.
2. *At onset:—*
   One Rigor with Vomiting.
   Abdominal Pain, sometimes in the iliac fossa.
   He is Cyanosed.
   The Pulse rate is about 100.
   The Temperature is elevated.
   A plastered Tongue.
   The Respirations are over 20 per minute.
   Rigidity of the belly wall muscles.
   Perhaps a dull note upon Percussion over lung.
   The Breath Sounds are altered.
3. *Symptoms and Signs which are normal:—*
   Bowels and Passage of Flatus.
   Micturition.
   Urine.
   Hernial Sites.
   Heart Apex Beat.
   Knee Jerks.
   Testes.
   Rectum.
   Heart Sounds.
4. *The Treatment is:—*
   Keep him in an even temperature.

Sit him up in bed.

Diet of milk, eggs, beef tea, and milk puddings.

Ammonium carbonate in 5-grain doses, every 4 hours.

Stimulants, if required.

Linseed poultice to the chest for any acute pain.

(*page 23*)

ACUTE PLEURISY, simulating an Acute Abdominal Lesion.

1. *At onset:—*

Several Shiverings.

Pain; local or in the abdomen, or both.

Pain increased during inspiration.

Sometimes Vomiting.

Elevation of Temperature.

Respirations over 20 per minute.

Dull note on Percussion over lung.

Sometimes Rigidity of belly wall.

The Heart may be displaced laterally by pleural effusion.

Pleural Friction and altered breath sounds are heard upon auscultation.

2. *Symptoms and Signs which are normal:—*

Bowels and Passage of Flatus.

Micturition.

Urine.

Hernial Sites.

Heart Apex Beat.

Knee Jerks.

Testes.

Rectum.

Heart Sounds.

3. *The Treatment is:—*

Bed.

Milk, beef tea, eggs, and milk puddings.

Linseed poultices to the chest for acute pain.

(*page 24*)

ACUTE DILATATION OF THE HEART, simulating an Acute
Abdominal Lesion.

79

1. *Prior to onset:—*
   Shortness of breath.
   Palpitation.
2. *At onset:—*
   Epigastric Pain, and vomiting.
   Shortness of Breath.
   Palpitation.
   Cyanosis.
   Pulse rate increased; beats are missed at the wrist pulse.
   Respirations are increased.
   The Urine contains albumen.
   The Heart Apex Beat is displaced into the axilla, if is diffuse
      and difficult to actually define.
   The area of Heart Dullness is increased.
   The legs are probably swollen.
   The Heart Sounds are altered.
   The Breath Sounds at the lung bases are altered.
3. *Symptoms and Signs which are normal:—*
   Bowels and Passage of Flatus.
   Micturition.
   Hernial Sites.
   No belly wall Rigidity.
   Knee Jerks.
   Testes.
   Rectum.
4. *The Treatment is:—*
   Absolute rest in bed.
   A saline purgative.
   Stimulants, if required.

(*page 25*)

   ACUTE PYELITIS, with Inflamed URETERS, simulating Acute
                           Appendicitis.
N.B.—It is usually bi-lateral.

1. *At onset:—*
   Often a Rigor, which may be repeated.
   Acute Pain beginning at the posterior renal area, which
      radiates *downwards* round the flank towards the groin (*see*
      page 42).

Sometimes the renal pain is worse on a deep inspiration.

Vomiting.

Elevated Temperature.

Increased Frequency of micturition.

        is hyper-acid in reaction.

Urine there is a deposit of pus and mucus.

        contains albumen.

There is a Tender Spot at the posterior renal area, usually on both sides.

There is Rigidity over the kidney.

There is Rigidity over the iliac fossa or fossae.

2. *Symptoms and Signs which are normal:—*

    Passage of Flatus.

    Pulse Rate.

    Respirations.

    Hernial Sites.

    Heart Apex Beat.

    Knee Jerks.

    Testes.

    Heart Sounds.

    Breath Sounds.

(*page 26*)

3. *The Treatment is:—*

    Keep the bowels well opened.

    Bed.

    Give potassium citrate or potassium bicarbonate in 30-grain doses every four hours until the urine is alkaline.

    Salol, in 5-grain doses three times daily.

    Milk, egg, and milk pudding diet.

    Six pints (or more) of fluid daily, *e.g.*, milk, barley water, plain water.

(*page 27*)

ACUTE EPIDIDYMITIS, simulating an Acute Abdominal Lesion.

1. *Prior to onset:—*

    He has recently acquired acute Gonorrhoea.

2. *At onset:*—

>Often a Rigor.
>Acute Pain in the testis, radiating *upwards* towards the kidney of the same side.
>Sometimes increased Frequency of micturition.
>Enlarged acutely Tender epididymis.
>Tenderness of the spermatic cord.
>Tenderness over the inguinal canal.
>Intra-cellular Diplococci in the stained urethral discharge.
>Elevated Temperature.

3. *Symptoms and Signs which are normal:*—

>Bowels and Passage of Flatus.
>Respirations.
>Hernial Sites.
>*No* posterior renal area tenderness.
>Heart Apex Beat.
>Knee Jerks.
>Heart Sounds.
>Breath Sounds.

4. *The Treatment is:*—

>Rest in bed.
>Support the scrotum on a small pillow.
>Give purgative.
>Give salol, 5 grains, three times daily.
>Paint glycerine and belladonna (B.P.) on to the scrotum over the affected testis, also over the inguinal canal of the same side.

(*page 28*)

TABES DORSALIS, with a "GASTRIC CRISIS."

1. *Prior to onset, of Abdominal Symptoms:*—

>Unsteadiness upon his feet when walking in the dark.

2. *At onset:*—

>Acute abdominal Pain.
>Vomiting.
>Rigidity of the belly wall.
>Absence of the Knee Jerks.
>Unsteadiness on the feet when his eyes are shut.

The Pupils do not react to light.
3. *Symptoms and Signs which are normal:—*
        Passage of Flatus.
        Pulse Rate.
        Temperature.
        Tongue.
        Respirations.
        Hernial Sites.
        Heart Apex Beat.
        Testes.
        Rectum.
        Heart Sounds.
        Breath Sounds.
4. *The Treatment is:—*
        Bed.
        Symptomatic. *e.g.*, apply poultices for the abdominal pain.

(*page 29*)
    INTERNAL BLEEDING from a ruptured VISCUS, or from a large
BLOOD VESSEL.

1. *At onset:—*
        History of an Accident.
        Abdominal Pain.
        Shock, he has a cold sweating head, and his pupils are dilated.
        Anaemia, it is especially noticeable of the lips.
        Restlessness.
        Pulse rate gradually and progressively increasing.
        Haematuria, if there is a ruptured kidney.
        Rigidity of the belly wall, if a ruptured viscus.
        Perhaps shifting Dullness on percussion of the flanks.

2. *Symptoms and Signs which are normal:—*
        Bowels and Passage of Flatus.
        Temperature.
        Hernial Sites.
        Heart Apex Beat.
        Knee Jerks.
        Testes.

Rectum.
Heart Sounds.
Breath Sounds.
3. *The Treatment is:*—
Immediate Operation.
Do not give stimulants, this will increase the bleeding.

(*page 30*)

RUPTURED BLADDER.
N.B.—It is often associated with a Fractured Pelvis.

1. *At onset:*—
History of an Accident to region of the pelvis with a full bladder.
Shock.
Passage of a little Bloody Urine, or none at all.
The Pulse rate progressively increases.
Muscular Rigidity in the hypogastrium.
Tenderness in the hypogastrium.
2. *Symptoms and Signs which are normal:*—
Bowels and Passage of Flatus.
Temperature.
Respirations.
Hernial Sites.
Heart Apex Beat.
Knee Jerks.
Testes.
Heart Sounds.
Breath Sounds.
3. *The Treatment is:*—
Immediate Operation.

(*page 31*)

FRACTURED RIBS, the lower ones and in front.

1. *At onset:*—
History of an Accident.
Abdominal Pain increased on respiration.
The Respirations are increased and shallow.

Rigidity of the belly wall.

Crepitus heard or felt over the broken ribs.

2. *Symptoms and Signs which are normal:—*

Bowels and Passage of Flatus.

Micturition.

Pulse Rate.

Temperature.

Tongue.

Urine.

Hernial Sites.

Heart Apex Beat.

Knee Jerks.

Testes.

Rectum.

Heart Sounds.

3. *The Treatment is:—*

Rest in bed.

Apply strips of adhesive strapping to the chest wall at the end of an expiration, long enough to extend across the middle line back and front.

(page 32)

ACUTE INFECTIOUS FEVERS, simulating acute abdominal lesion (*see* pages 59 to 62).

1. *At onset:—*

Acute abdominal Pain.

Vomiting.

Headache.

Possibly a "bad cold."

Sore Throat.

Elevated Temperature.

The Pulse rate is quick.

Furred Tongue.

Possibly enlarged tender glands behind angle of jaw.

2. *Symptoms and Signs which are normal:—*

Passage of Flatus.

Micturition.

Hernial Sites.

Heart Apex Beat.
Knee Jerks.
Testes.
Rectum.
Heart Sounds.
No rigidity of the belly wall.
No rash at onset.

3. *For Treatment, see* page 59.

Clinical Notes For Surgeon Probationers: (Part II)

(*page 33*)

PART II.
NOTES ON SOME OTHER AILMENTS
LIKELY TO BE SEEN IN
A PERSON OF NAVAL RATING AGE.

PULSE:—
There are five points to be determined:—
  (1) Rate per minute; the normal is 72.
  (2) Rhythm, *i.e.*, if the succession of beats ir regular or irregular.
  (3) Tension, *i.e.*, if it is high or low.
  (4) Volume, if it is large or small.
  (5) The condition of the artery walls, *i.e.*, are they thickened or not.

THE PHYSICAL SIGNS OF A TUMOUR:—
Learn, remember, and use the points in the order given here; they are often alone sufficient to diagnose between a benign and a malignant tumour. These points are:—
  (1) *Consistence.*—If hard, soft, elastic, or fluctuating.
  (2) *Surface.*—If smooth or nodular.
  (3) *Edge.*—If the edge of the tumour can be abruptly defined, or if it shelves off into the normal surrounding tissues.
  (4) *Relation to surrounding parts.*—If the tumour is adherent to the superficial structures, *e.g.*, the skin, *or* to the deeper, or to any special tissues.

(*page 34*)
(*a*) RECTAL QUESTIONS REFER TO:—
  (1) *Pain.*— Its site; whether it comes before, during, after, or independent of defaecation.
  (2) *Prolapse.*—Whether any swelling prolapses through the anus, and, if so, whether it prolapses before, during, after or

87

independent of defaecation.

(3) *Discharge.*—The nature of any discharge, *e.g.*, blood, mucus (which looks like clear jelly), or pus; whether the discharge comes before, during, after, or independent of defaecation; if there is blood, whether this plasters the whole motion equally, or if it appears as a long streak upon one side of the stool.

(4) *Defaecation.*—Whether there is constipation or diarrhoea; whether the motions are normal in size and shape.

HAEMORRHOIDS (or PILES):—

Haemorrhoids may be seen but not felt unless they are thrombosed. A patient may come complaining of "piles" when there is nothing either to see, or feel. To prove the presence or absence of the condition, give a soap-and-water enema and examine immediately after it has acted; the straining makes piles more prominent.

In uncomplicated haemorrhoids the symptoms usually are—

(1) Absence of pain.

(2) They often prolapse after defaecation and require to be replaced manually.

(3) Bleeding towards the end of defaecation.

(4) Constipation.

Treatment:— In the early stages the patient should arrange so that his bowels are moved once daily, preferably just before bedtime; in advanced cases an operation will be required.

(*a*) Under each rectal disease described here, the answers to these questions are given under the headings (1), (2), (3), (4).

(*page 35*)

Before advising operation first satisfy yourself that:—

(1) The heart sounds are normal.

(2) The liver is not enlarged.

(3) The spleen is not enlarged.

(4) No abnormal swelling can be felt in the abdomen.

(5) The rectum is free from malignant growth.

THROMBOSED HAEMORRHOIDS:—

Thrombosed (or inflamed) haemorrhoids have a sudden onset, the symptoms usually being:—

(1) Constant pain at the anus.

(2) The thrombosed pile is an elastic, smooth surfaced, tender swelling, which is always present at the anus at this stage.

(3) There may be a discharge, but only if there is any ulceration.

(4) Constipation.

Treatment:— Rest in bed. If a large mass has recently prolapsed, try by gentle pressure to get it back into the rectum; apply hot boracic fomentations to the anus every four hours; get the bowels well moved once daily, and immediately afterwards to sit in a tub of hot water.

An ordinary case will be well in three days, by this time the thrombosed pile will have disappeared inside the anus. A large irreducible mass tends to become gangrenous and may require operation.

FISSURE-IN-ANO:—

The symptoms usually are—

(1) Agonising pain, coming on immediately after defaecation and lasting at least for half an hour.

(2) There is a "sentinel" pile visible at the anus.

(3) The motion is streaked with blood along one side.

(4) Marked constipation which is often voluntary, for the patient, terrified of the pain after defaecation, prefers to put off the evil day.

(page 36)

Treatment:— Gentle laxatives followed by the application of unguentum hammamelis within the anus may be tried, but most cases require division of the external sphincter ani before the condition can be really remedied.

FISTULA-IN-ANO:—

There is usually:—

(1) Discomfort after defaecation.

(2) No prolapse.

(3) A constant discharge of pus and blood, independent of defaecation, from the sinus; flatus and faeces may also discharge through the sinus if the fistula is a complete one.

(4) Constipation.

RECTAL POLYPUS:—

There is usually:—

(1) No pain.

(2) The polypus prolapses during defaecation, but can usually be

easily replaced.

(3) An excess of mucus accompanying the stool.

(4) It does not affect the action of the bowels.

CARCINOMA OF THE RECTUM:—

There is usually:—

(1) Perpetual discomfort in the rectum; it being a sensation of failure to empty it rather than pain.

(2) The carcinoma will not prolapse but the accompanying haemorrhoids may do so.

(3) Blood-stained offensive discharge with the motions.

(4) Constipation alternating with diarrhoea; the motion may be altered in calibre, shape, and consistence, due to narrowing of the bowel at the site of the growth. The usual story is of frequent and urgent attempts at defaecation, followed by the passage of only flatus, and a teaspoonful of offensive fluid motion.

(page 37)

RETENTION OF URINE:—

Common causes are:—

In young men	Prostatic abscess.
In middle aged men	Stricture of the urethra.
In old men	Enlarged prostate.

The *Treatment* depends upon the cause of the retention, but whatever the cause relief must be given.

If due to a prostatic abscess, this will be felt by rectal examination as a soft elastic tender swelling bulging the anterior rectal wall. First try sitting the patient in a tub of hot water to micturate there if that be possible. If this fails, thoroughly cleanse the end of the penis with potassium permanganate solution (strength 2 grains to 10 ounces of warm water), then syringe out the urethra with the same solution before passing the catheter.

If due to a stricture, give 30 minims of tinctura opii before using the hot tub; while in this, attempts should be made to micturate. If these fail, pass a catheter as far as it will go and replace him in the tub; merely touching the face of the stricture is sometimes sufficient to start the stream.

If these measures fail, surgical relief must be arranged for without delay.

(*a*) URINARY QUESTIONS REFER TO:—

  (1) *Frequency:*—How often is urine passed by day and by night. It is abnormal to pass water regularly during the night.

 (*b*)(2) *Pain:*—Where is it; state its relation to micturition; whether pain precedes the flow, accompanies the flow, or follows it.

(*a*) Under each urinary disease described here, the answers to these questions are given under the headings (1), (2), (3), (4).

  (*b*) *See* page 42.

(*page 38*)

  (3) *Character of Stream:*—Is it single or double; is it normal in calibre; has it normal force; is there straining to get it away; are there sudden stoppages followed by resumption of the flow. Always watch the patient pass urine, do not accept his word for observable facts.

  (4) *Character of the Urine:*— Is it offensive; is it clear or cloudy; does it contain blood; has it a deposit upon standing; if it contains blood or pus, does this precede or follow the flow of urine.

In GENERAL CYSTITIS:—

There is usually:—

  (1) Increased frequency of micturition day and night.

  (2) Pain in the hypogastrium before micturition, and in the perinaeum after micturition.

  (3) The stream is single, normal in calibre and force, and there is urgency to micturate.

  (4) The urine is cloudy, there is a yellowish deposit after standing, and it may contain blood.

In STONE IN THE BLADDER:—

There is usually:—

  (1) Increased frequency of micturition, but only when the patient moves about.

  (2) Pain in the perinaeum and at the end of the penis after micturition.

  (3) The stream is single, normal in calibre and force, but there may be interruptions in the flow, due to the stone moving into the bladder outlet and blocking it temporarily.

91

(4) There may be haematuria after exercise, and at the end of micturition, due to the rough surface of the stone tearing small blood vessels on the base of the bladder.

(page 39)

In uncomplicated STRICTURE OF THE URETHRA:—

There is usually:—

(1) Increased frequency of micturition, day and night.
(2) No pain, except perhaps uneasiness in the perinaeum during micturition.
(3) The stream may be forked; it is diminished in calibre; its force is not impaired; there is straining to get the urine away; and dribbling of urine after the act appears to be finished.
(4) Normal urine, though it may contain purulent threads.

In uncomplicated TUMOURS OF THE BLADDER:—

There is usually:—

(1) No increased frequency of micturition.
(2) No pain.
(3) A normal stream flow.
(4) The urine contains blood in quantity, but only intermittently, and it appears at the end of micturition, due to the bladder wall contracting down upon the growth.

JOINTS:—

When investigating any joint case keep in mind that the following structures enter into the formation of a joint:—

(1) Bone.
(2) Cartilage.
(3) Synovial membrane.
(4) Ligaments.

When examining a joint always compare the normal joint with the abnormal one.

An inflamed joint presents the ordinary signs of an inflammation (*see* page 41).

Inflamed bone causes bad pain at night, but may not during the day. Chronic inflammation produces thickening which can be felt in an accessible bone.

(page 40)

Palpate, if accessible, the margins of the joint for any "lipping," *i.e.*, overgrowth of cartilage covering the joint surface.

Inflamed synovial membrane pain is worse for exercise and better for rest; when this membrane is inflamed the swelling obliterates the normal outlines of the joint.

Any abnormal range of movement means a damaged joint ligament.

Wasting of muscles above and below a joint nearly always means an organic lesion in that joint.

As a routine, examine the urethra for signs of gonorrhoea in all joint conditions.

Acute joint inflammation which flits about from joint to joint, *suggests Rheumatic Fever.*

Acute joint inflammation which is confined to one joint *suggests Gonorrhoeal Arthritis.*

Dental caries and chronic joint inflammation are often associated; therefore in joint conditions examine the teeth.

An accident to a knee joint, where this is forced inwards while in a position of flexion, accompanied by acute pain, inability to completely extend the joint, followed by the joint becoming distended with fluid within a few hours — *suggests a Ruptured Semilunar Cartilage.*

A joint which is painful, creaks on movement, and is stiff after resting but which gets better after it has been exercised a little — *suggests Osteo Arthritis.*

Should a joint require rest as treatment for any length of time, always immobilise it in the position most useful to the patient if it subsequently should become stiff; *e.g.*, immobilise:—

The wrist, in slight extension.

The shoulder, with a good pad of wool in the axilla, the arm being vertical.

The hip, with the limb straight out.

The knee, just short of full extension.

The ankle, at a right angle.

(page 41)

ACUTE EPIPHYSITIS or ACUTE OSTEO-MYELITIS:—

A person under 22 years of age who has sudden violent pain and other signs of an acute inflammation near the end of a long bone, together with high temperature, quick pulse rate, and sometimes delirium — is probably suffering from *Acute Epiphysitis.* This condition may be regarded as identical with Acute Osteo-Myelitis.

The patient must be promptly removed to Hospital for surgical treatment.

INFLAMMATION:

It is characterised by:—

Pain.

Redness.

Swelling.

Heat.

Tenderness.

Impaired function.

The *end results* of every inflammation are either:—

(1) Resolution; or

(2) Fibrosis; or

(3) Partial destruction; or

(4) Total destruction.

The causes of Chronic Inflammation are:—

Tubercle.   ) The commonest causes.

Syphilis.   )

Trauma.

Rheumatism.

Alcohol.

Gout.

(page 42)

PAIN and TENDERNESS:—

Pain may be acute or subacute.

As a guide to the severity of pain, remember that severe pain makes a patient shout out, groan, roll about, vomit and sweat.

Stomach Ulcer Pain is felt in the epigastrium, and it radiates too in between the shoulder blades.

In *Duodenal Ulcer* there is a tender spot one inch to the right and one inch above the level of the umbilicus.

In *Appendicitis* there is tenderness at a spot one-third of the distance from the lower end of a line drawn from the right anterior superior spine to the umbilicus, *i.e.*, McBurney's Point.

Bladder (excluding the base) Pain is referred to the hypogastrium.

Bladder (base only) Pain is felt in the perinaeum, along the urethra and at the end of the penis.

Kidney Pain is felt at the "posterior renal area." This area is a well

94

defined spot (which can be covered by a finger tip), formed by the junction of the outer border of the erector spinae muscle with the lower border of the last rib. This spot should always be palpated in the routine examination of the abdomen.

Epididymitis Pain radiates upwards from the testis towards the kidney of the same side.

Diseased Vertebra Pain is referred along the intercostal nerves to the front of the abdomen.

Hip-joint Pain is often felt at the knee.

ABSCESS:—

A collection of pus (forming an abscess which may be unconcealed or concealed), following an acute inflammation, *e.g.*, an appendix abscess, usually presents three cardinal features:—

(1) There are night sweats.

(2) There is loss of flesh.

(3) There is a "swinging" temperature, *i.e.*, it is high at night and normal in the morning.

(page 43)
HEADACHE:—

When a patient feels unwell, has a headache, sore throat, is feverish and perhaps vomits — examine the pharynx and tonsils for a focus, and be on the look out for a rash.

Intense headache associated with vomiting, retraction of the head, and high temperature, with the patient lying on his side and the knees drawn up — *suggests Cerebro-Spinal Meningitis.*

Supra-orbital headache with signs of inflammation, lachrymation, photophobia, and a small pupil which is sluggish in movement to light — *indicates Acute Iritis.*

A frontal headache which gets worse towards night *suggests an Error of Refraction*, and a need to get the patient's eyes tested.

A frontal headache persistently present upon awakening in the morning, associated with thirst, polyuria, and loss of flesh, is evidence of *Uraemia.*

Headache, with a moist brown furred tongue, is caused by *Constipation.*

VOMITING:—

The points to note about vomiting are:—

(1) If forceful or not.

(2) Its taste; if bitter, yeasty, &c.

(3) The quantity vomited at one time.

(4) Its consistence; if digested or partly digested food, if it is watery, biliary, or faecal.

(5) If it contains blood.

(6) If offensive.

In every case of serious vomiting never forget to examine the hernial sites for a possible strangulated hernia.

If a patient habitually vomits more than he has eaten at the last meal, it suggests that he is suffering from a dilated stomach.

(page 44)

Material like yeast floating upon the surface of the vomit is evidence that the stomach cannot empty itself, and that fermentation is going on.

For practical purposes, vomit with a faecal odour may be regarded as an indication of intestinal obstruction.

COUGH:—

The onset of a cough, at first without expectoration, accompanied by a raw feeling during inspiration behind the sternum — *suggests Acute Bronchitis.* Put the patient to bed, keep him in an even temperature, apply hot poultices to the chest to relieve the pain, and, if possible, have a kettle constantly steaming away to moisten the cabin atmosphere; give him light diet only.

A chronic morning cough which begins when the patient awakes, and continues incessantly until a varying amount of viscid expectoration is brought up, *indicates Chronic Bronchitis.* After he has finished bringing up the expectoration, there is only a slight cough for the remainder of the 24 hours. The secretion (*i.e.,* the expectoration) collects in the bronchi during sleep.

When the patient complains of a constant *Cough with expectoration,* if the evidence of lung tuberculosis is negative, ammonium carbonate in 5-grain doses is indicated; this aids the expulsion of the secretion in the bronchi.

When a patient complains of a constant *Cough without expectoration,* if no abnormal physical signs are present in the chest give the following mixture three times daily:—

Potassium Nitrate   5 grains.

Liquid Ext. of Liquorice	5 minims.
Wine of Ipecacuanha	10 minims.
Compount Tinct. of Camphor	20 minims.
Mucilage of Tragacanth	1 drachm.
Water to	1 fluid ounce.

If a patient coughs up blood, regard it as an indication of *lung tuber-culosis* until the contrary is proved.

(page 45)
JAUNDICE:—

Jaundice is due to bile absorption by the minute lymphatics of the liver, a sequel to some obstruction to its normal passage. The bile then reaches the general circulation *via* the thoracic duct.

Should jaundice, the presence of bile in the urine, and clay-coloured motions follow an acute gastritis, it means that the inflammation has spread from the stomach to the duodenum. The orifice of the ampulla of Vater has become obstructed, which results in the bile becoming dammed back.

A more common cause of jaundice is probably gall-stones, only this is associated with attacks of biliary colic.

Daylight is required to detect jaundice.

The *treatment* is — treat the cause.

BLEEDING FROM A GASTRIC OR DUODENAL ULCER:—

Haematamesis means vomited blood. It is rarely bright red in colour unless there is profuse bleeding; it usually has the appearance of coffee grounds, due to the mixture of blood and gastric juice.

Melaena means blood appearing in the stools, which are then a black colour. Blood changes its colour during its passage along the intestine. Medicine containing bismuth also makes a black coloured stool, there-fore question the patient about his taking medicine if he complains of melaena.

Haematemesis is most likely to be due to a gastric ulcer.

Melaena (without haematemesis) is most likely to be due to a duo-denal ulcer.

(page 46)
ANTISEPSIS AND ASEPSIS:—

Some years before the Franco-Prussian War, the famous French chemist, Louis Pasteur, proved that putrefaction was caused "by particles suspended in the air.'' Lord Lister used this information when searching for a means of preventing putrefaction in wounds, and of those in compound fractures in particular. At that time nearly all wounds — operation and otherwise — suppurated, and the mortality from sepsis alone was very high. He used Carbolic Acid, 1 in 20; his success with this solution was instant, it revolutionised surgery and was the beginning of the *Antiseptic Era*, *i.e.*, the method of destroying organisms, which caused sepsis, by means of chemicals.

Later, it was shown that the healing of a clean wound might be retarded by the introduction of chemicals into it, and there dawned the *Aseptic Era*, *i.e.*, the destruction of septic organisms by heat, applied to surgical instruments, dressings, &c.

Although probably true that chemicals may delay healing in a wound, should any septic organisms be present, the antiseptic has a good chance of destroying them, while the aseptic method does not give this chance. In other words it is much wiser, especially for inexperienced Surgeon Probationers, to use the antiseptic routine; it is safer and will prove much more efficient.

The surgical instruments should be actually boiling for at least a quarter of an hour, then transferred to 1 in 20 solution of carbolic acid and used direct out of this. All gauze and wool dressings should contain some antiseptic.

LOTIONS:—

Normal saline solution is made by adding one teaspoonful of common salt to one pint of water; sterilise it by boiling.

(page 47)

Boracic acid is only mildly antiseptic in its action. To make boracic lotion, add one teaspoonful of the powder to one pint of water which has been boiled.

Carbolic acid, 1 in 20 solution, is a strong antiseptic. It can be used for the skin, also for mopping out the depths of a wound. It is made by mixing one ounce of Acid Carbolic Liqufactum with 19 ounces of water.

Remember that the germicidal powers of all antiseptics are neutralised in the presence of much albumen, *e.g.*, blood.

Iodine, in the presence of lotions or dressings containing mercury, is liable to produce bad blistering of the skin.

A PLAN FOR THE TREATMENT OF ALL WOUNDS:—

All war wounds are likely to be septic; by conscientiously treating the

98

wound under antiseptic precautions the Surgeon Probationer may limit this; where he does succeed it is a great feather in his cap.

1. Boil the instruments likely to be required, and get ready lotions, ligatures, dressings, razor, and splints.

2. Cleanse hands which will be employed in dressing a case or at an operation. Use soap and hot water, followed by rubbing turpentine, then methylated spirits, well in; then rinse in an antiseptic lotion.

3. Place a mop wrung out of an antiseptic (*e.g.*, carbolic acid 1 in 20 in solution) into the gaping wound; shave an adequate area round it; then cleanse the skin by either (*a*) similar to the hands, or (*b*) carbolic acid 1 in 20 solution *only*.

4. Re-cleanse the hands.

5. Clip and ligature any large bleeding points; rely upon pressure from an antiseptic gauze packing to check venous or capillary oozing.

6. If there is a small cleanly incised would, rub Borsal powder into it; close it with interrupted sutures, but do not place these too close together.

(*page 48*)

7. If it is a large wound, remove any visible foreign body, and rub Borsal powder thoroughly into every part of the depths of the wound with the finger. Do not attempt to bring the skin margins together with sutures; drainage is required, and a gaping wound drains well. Pack it with antiseptic gauze to check any oozing; cover the wound with antiseptic gauze and wool, then apply a bandage; evacuate to a hospital for further treatment.

8. If there is much pain or shock give morphia, grain ¼, hypodermically.

Matters are much hastened if the Doctor wears india rubber gloves, which have been sterilised by boiling. They should have a smooth surface, then constantly rinsing the gloved hands in carbolic acid 1 in 20 solution is sufficient to sterilise them for all practical purposes.

After an action there may not be anyone to fetch things for the Doctor. With a number of cases to attend to, he can only carry on quickly if he can himself get anything required for the dressing, even if it involves handling something which is not sterilised. Sepsis is fairly readily removed from a smooth glove surface by the strong antiseptic; bare fingers could not long tolerate a strong antiseptic as they would be quickly skinned.

SHOCK:—

The patient lies inert; he looks pallid, is in a cold sweat; his pupils are dilated; the pulse is fast and of feeble volume, and the temperature is subnormal.

Treat by hot applications (such as hot blankets and hot bottles), hot drinks, and inject hot coffee (temperature 100°F.) containing sugar slowly into the rectum with a Higginson syringe or through a catheter and funnel.

Do *not* give alcohol or strychnine unless you have excluded internal bleeding; if there is bleeding, to stimulate the patient means increasing the haemorrhage.

(page 49)
FRACTURES:—

Where you have a fractured bone, always examine for possible complications, by testing beyond the site of the fracture, (*a*) the pulse, (*b*) the skin, for absence of normal sensation, (*c*) voluntary movements of muscles, if this is possible, for detection of paralysis.

The Surgeon Probationer's duty is to render first aid and immobilise the fractured ends of the bone to prevent further injury. When at sea, probably the best method of accomplishing this in a case of fracture of the tibia, is to apply well-padded back and side splints to the leg, and swing the limb on a Salter's cradle; all these can be improvised if necessary.

A compound fracture *is treated* as is an ordinary wound plus a fracture.

If a patient complains of the bandage being too tight, remove and re-apply it; if this is neglected the consequences may be gangrene of the limb.
BURNS:—

Apply the Service picric acid dressing as directed. Remember that there is always much swelling after burns; therefore, attend to any complaints about a bandage being too tight. If you are too busy to attend to it yourself, detail someone to cut the bandage until you are free to go into the matter. Neglect of this may lead to gangrene under the bandage.
LUDWIG'S ANGINA:—

Is suppuration under the investing layer of the deep cervical fascia which prevents the pus from coming to the surface. The commonest cause is a carious tooth.

Treatment, by incision, must be prompt, owing to the danger of laryngeal obstruction and spreading sepsis under tension.

(page 50)

FOLLICULAR TONSILLITIS:—

Is due to the mouths of the tonsil follicles becoming blocked with a plug of pus. The symptoms are due to absorption of the poisons which are dammed up in the lumen of the follicle behind the "plug." These plugs can often be "sizzled" out by frequently gargling a solution containing two teaspoonfuls of hydrogen peroxide (20 volume) in a tumblerful of warm water.

(See also Diphtheria, page 61.)

CARBUNCLE AND BOIL:—

In determining whether the focus is a carbuncle or a boil, size is no guide, for either of them may be large or small. In both there is a local acutely inflamed area, each focus containing a slough.

A carbuncle is usually a *single focus* with multiple openings for the pus to escape.

Boils *are multiple*, but each one has a single opening.

Carbuncles and boils may be associated with diabetes, therefore test the urine for sugar as a routine.

The treatment of each condition, in the early stages, is frequently changed hot boracic fomentations.

WHITLOW:—

Is inflammation of a digit.

There are four varieties:—

    (1) *Subcuticular*, a blister containing pus.

    (2) *Subcutaneous*, in the subcutaneous tissue.

    (3) *Subperiosteal*, where the infection spreads to the bone.

    (4) *Thecal*, where the synovial tendon sheath is involved.

The thecal variety of the first and fifth digits of the hand are the most dangerous whitlows, especially the latter for the tendon synovial sheath always communicates with the palmar synovial tendon sheath.

The treatment of Whitlow is early incision, together with frequently changed hot boracic fomentations.

(*page 51*)
HERNIA:—

The *Usual* palpable hernial sites are: (1) in the inguinal area, (2) in the femoral region, and (3) at the umbilicus.

The *Unusual* palpable hernial sites are: (1) near the origin of the thigh adductor muscles (obturator hernia), (2) upon the buttock (gluteal hernia and sciatic hernia), and (3) just above the crest of the ilium (lumbar hernia).

Before recommending a patient for operation:—

    (1) Examine the chest for evidence of bronchitis.

    (2) Ask the four "urinary" questions.

    (3) Ask the four "rectal" questions.

A hernia can result from a chronic cough, from obstruction to micturition, or from obstruction to defaecation. The presence of any of these symptoms may be a contra-indication to operation, and remains a contra-indication until the cause can be removed.

VARICOSE VEINS:—

If they developed during the course of an acute infectious fever, *e.g.*, typhoid fever, operation is contra-indicated; it means that the deep veins of the limb have become blocked by thrombosis, and the superficial veins are doing their work; if these are operated upon, neighbouring veins will become varicose to replace those excised.

If there is thrombosis of a vein [phlebitis], there will be signs of an acute inflammation along the course of it. The treatment is physical rest and the frequent application of hot fomentations. Treatment by massage, or any energetic movements (*e.g.*, walking), are dangerous measures, for the blood clot may become dislodged with fatal consequences.

VARICOCELE:—

Before recommending an operation, examine the flank of the same side for an enlarged kidney; varicocele is sometimes secondary to a malignant growth of the kidney.

(*page 52*)
BACK PAIN AFTER AN INJURY:—

Ask the patient to bend down and touch his toes; notice whether the pain is worse "going down or coming back." If it is worse during flexion of the spine it suggests torn vertebral ligaments; if it is worse during extension of the spine it means muscle trouble, and usually lumbago.

Rigidity of the spinal column (*i.e.*, limitation of its movements due to pain) is evidence of the presence of some active mischief in the vertebrae.

OTITIS MEDIA:—

In acute pain in the ear, think of acute otitis media, and a boil in the external auditory meatus. The former may require prompt treatment, therefore evacuate the case to hospital; if it is not deep the latter may be seen as a pimple.

In a case of chronic discharging ear think of the onset of *Acute Mastoiditis*, if:—

(1) the ear discharge suddenly ceases;

(2) acute pain in the ear or behind the ear is complained of;

(3) the patient feels ill and looks ill;

(4) there is acute tenderness when the mastoid process is pressed with a finger tip:

The treatment is immediate operation.

CONJUNCTIVITIS:—

One of the commonest causes of conjunctivitis is the presence of a foreign body, *e.g.*, a speck of dust or metal. Thoroughly search for this under the eyelids, using cocaine if necessary. After its removal instil a few drops of castor oil.

Caustic potash or lime must be promptly removed from an eye, either with forceps or by flushing out with quantities of plain water. If the eye is so painful that the patient will not permit it to be touched, insert a

(*page 53*)
tabloid of cocaine to reduce the pain and tenderness. After removal of the caustic, instil a few drops of castor oil.

GONORRHOEAL OPHTHALMIA:—

This begins as a violent inflammation of the conjunctiva due to infection by the gonococcus. As prevention is much better than cure, every patient with gonorrhoea must be warned about the dangers of not washing his hands after they may have become soiled by the urethral discharge.

Onset of the condition:—

The eye feels inflamed and it smarts.

The conjunctiva and eyelids both show signs of an acute inflammation, the swollen condition of these being a marked feature.

There is soon a profuse discharge.

Treatment:—

The condition is a serious one; it must be dealt with energetically, otherwise the patient may lose his sight.

Should circumstances not permit his being immediately evacuated to a hospital, the following is a line of treatment:-

(1) Hermetically seal off the sound eye by placing over it an ordinary watch glass whose margins are firmly secured to the skin by strips of adhesive strapping.

(2) Remove the pus by irrigations every hour, using two pints of a hot saturated solution of boracic acid, *or* a 1 in 10,000 hot solution of mercury perchloride, or mercury biniodide. Use an irrigator with india rubber tubing attached. With the disengaged hand evert the eyelids in order to flush all the conjunctival recesses.

(*page 54*)

(3) Instil six drops of a 1 per cent. solution of silver nitrate into the eye every four hours.

(4) Should an ulcer form about the centre of the cornea, insert one tabloid of atropine sulphate every four hours.

(5) If, however, an ulcer forms upon the cornea away from its centre, insert one tabloid of eserine sulphate every six hours.

VENEREAL DISEASE:—

In suspected venereal disease, always make a routine examination, and obtain an answer to the following points:—

(1) Is there any discharge from the urethral meatus?

(2) Are there any penile ulcers? If so, how many are there, and what is their exact condition?

(3) Is there any enlargement of the lymphatic glands of the groin, of the axilla, or at the epitrochlear area?

(4) Is there any rash upon the chest or abdominal wall?

(5) Are there any ulcers or white patches on the posterior pharyngeal wall, upon the fauces, or upon the mucous membrane of the mouth?

Gonorrhoea usually appears as a urethral discharge 3 to 5 days after sexual contact. The discharge soon becomes profuse and of a creamy yellow colour; as a rule there is smarting pain during micturition.

Syphilis usually appears from 10 days to 8 weeks (commonly 3 weeks) after sexual intercourse, as a single focus — a chancre — which is hard upon palpation.

In the ordinary way gonococci do not travel in the blood. If these organisms do gain the blood stream, they usually settle down *either* in some joint, and cause an arthritis, *or* in the fascia of the sole of the foot or forearm, which is termed *Gonorrhoeal Rheumatism*.

(page 55)

The spirochaetae, the organisms causing syphilis, gain the blood stream and are therefore carried to every part of the body. This explains the generalised rash, the sore throat, the lymphatic enlargement, &c., of syphilis.

Chancroid usually appears as several excavated ulcers upon the glans penis, 2 to 3 days after intercourse. Chancroid ulcers are *not* hard on palpation.

ACUTE BRIGHT'S DISEASE:—

This may begin:—(*a*) with puffiness of the eyelids upon awakening in the morning, *or* (*b*) with headache, nausea, furred tongue, and pain in the lumbar region. In either case there is scanty urine, which contains much albumen.

The *treatment* is:—

Rest in bed in an even temperature.

A jalap purgative.

A diet of milk only.

Abundance of plain water and of barley water to drink.

A mixture containing ammonium acetate and spirits of nitrous ether, to encourage perspiration, and increase the amount of urine.

A large hot linseed poultice to the loins.

ACUTE RHEUMATISM:—

There is a feeling of "seediness," and frequently of sore throat prior to onset. The temperature is elevated. Acute pain, with swelling of the joints which are exquisitely tender, follows; the inflammation flits from joint to joint — a characteristic feature of the disease. There are profuse sweats, acid in reaction, when tested with litmus paper. Endocarditis is a frequent accompaniment.

The *treatment* is:—

Absolute rest in bed, in a flannel night shirt, between blankets.

A fluid diet and plenty of it.

105

Wrap the affected joints in hot cotton wool.
Give a saline aperient.

(page 56)
Give sodium salicylate in 20-grain doses every four hours.
Should the temperature rise above 105°F., a cold water sponge
bath should be given every eight hours until the high fever abates.
SCIATICA:—
In sciatica, the patient lying upon his back, cannot flex his thigh
beyond a right angle with the leg fully extended. Moreover, the thigh
pain is always behind the line of the trousers seam.
Always ask the four "rectal" questions and make a rectal examina-
tion; sciatica is sometimes a sequel to a malignant growth in the pelvis.
A NERVOUS "JUMPY" PATIENT:—
A good prescription for such a patient, who is, perhaps, not sleeping
well, or who has not quite recovered from the effects of a naval action,
is:—

Potassium Bromide	12 grains.
Spirit, Ammon. Aromaticus	15 minims.
Decoction of Aloes to	½ ounce.

The amount of aloes must be reduced if it is too purgative. An
essential part of the treatment is that the patient be kept in ignor-
ance of the composition of his medicine.
FLATULENT DYSPEPSIA:-
Is characterised by a feeling of general lassitude, discomfort in the
epigastrium after meals, a bad taste in the mouth, flatulence, irregular
action of the bowels and a furred tongue. It can often be relieved by a
course of the following medicine:—

Salol	5 grains
Magnesium Carbonate	10 grains.
Pulv Rhei	10 grains.

(page 57)

Soda Bicarbonate	10 grains.
Tragacanth Mucilage	30 minims.
Spirit, Ammon. Aromaticus	10 minims.
Aqua Menth. Pip to	1 fluid ounce.

This is not a pleasant mixture to take, but its effects are good!

THE "SHIP'S PAINTER" (*see* also page 21):—

He spends his life amongst paint, therefore any ailment complained of, particularly constipation or colic, suggests *Lead Poisoning* as a possible cause. A blue line of the gums around the teeth confirms this suspicion.

DIARRHOEA:—

Examine the abdomen and rectum for a cause. If no cause can be discovered, ascertain if the motions are offensive or not. If they are offensive give one ounce of castor oil; if they are not offensive, give 20 minims of tinct. opii as a single draught.

PEDICULOSIS:—

The nits (*i.e.*, the eggs) are seen to be attached to the hair anywhere, but particularly of the scalp and pubes.

For *treatment* apply the following ointment, spread upon plain lint, to the affected area:—

Hydrargyrum Ammoniata   10 grains.
Vaseline to   1 ounce.

Give orders for the patient's clothes to be baked in an oven or in a disinfector, and for the latrine seats to be scrubbed daily with a disinfectant.

SCABIES:—

The patient complains of itching in the webs between the fingers, the front of the wrists, and at the axillary folds, &c., especially at night time. Examine these areas when evidence of scratching and of vesicles may be found.

Treatment.—Upon three consecutive nights he should have a hot soap and water bath; upon getting out of this he should rub one

(*page 58*)

ounce of unguentum sulphuris into the skin. For the succeeding ten days the same ointment recommended for pediculosis should be applied, after the soap and water bath. Clothing should be baked in a disinfector, and during treatment old clothes should be worn.

Five days' treatment cures the great majority of cases.

SKIN DISEASES GENERALLY:—

Probably the best all round ointment for skin diseases where the Surgeon Probationer cannot make a diagnosis is the one given for the treatment of pediculosis (*see* p. 57). To apply it, it should be spread upon plain lint.

RASHES:—

Common varieties of rashes include:—

(1) An Erythema; this is a reddening of the skin, and may be diffuse or distributed in patches.

(2) A Papule, is an ordinary solid pimple.

(3) A Vesicle, is a pimple containing clear fluid.

(4) A Pustule, is a pimple containing pus.

Points to note about any rash:—

(1) Its starting place.

(2) Its distribution on the body, if symmetrical or otherwise.

(3) Its appearance, *i.e.*, is it an erythema, or a collection of papules, vesicles, pustules, &c.

(4) Is it nodular, smooth, rough or indurated to the touch.

The rash, associated with an acute infectious fever, usually appears upon a definite day after the onset of the illness. In virulent infections, the rash is frequently livid or purple in colour.

(page 59)

ACUTE INFECTIOUS FEVERS:—

In the routine examination:—

(1) Look for signs of acute inflammation or of ulceration on the pharyngeal walls, the tonsils, the fauces, palate, and inside of the cheeks.

(2) Look for patches of white membrane in the same situations.

(3) Examine the skin all over for a rash.

(4) Take his temperature, pulse rate, and see the tongue.

The *treatment* is:—

Isolate the patient.

Quarantine all "contacts" for the prescribed period. Infection is carried by contact with the patient or with his garments, &c.

Before commencing treatment a "throat swab" should be taken for bacteriological examination.

Keep the patient in bed until his temperature has been normal for at any rate a few days.

If there is a "sore throat" an antiseptic gargle must be used frequently, *e.g.*, a 1 in 80 warm solution of carbolic acid.

Give a purgative (except in typhoid fever).

Light diet.

Watch for any complication. Examine the urine periodically until convalescence is established.

CHICKEN POX:—

The *rash* appears upon the day of onset of the illness. (*a*)

It has no typical starting place.

It has no typical distribution.

Each focus begins as a papule, turns to a vesicle, then possibly becomes a pustule.

The foci are not hard on palpation.

The vesicle completely collapses when it is pricked.

(*a*) *i.e.*, the Patient is taken ill upon a Monday and the Rash appears upon that Monday.

(*page 60*)

SCARLET FEVER:—

The *rash* usually appears upon the day after onset of the illness.(*a*)

It appears first upon the chest.

It spreads to the limbs, &c.

It is a vivid scarlet erythema.

SMALL POX:—

The *rash* usually appears upon the second day after onset of the illness.(*b*)

It has no typical starting place.

It has no typical distribution.

Each focus begins as a papule, turns to a vesicle, then always becomes a pustule which has a depression upon its apex (umbilication).

The papule feels like a lead shot embedded in the skin.

The vesicle does *not* collapse when it is pricked.

MEASLES:—

The *rash* usually appears on the third day after the onset of the illness.(*c*)

It starts upon the face.

It spreads from there to the body.

It consists of a collection of raised red patches which tend to run together.

It does not become papular nor pustular; it is smooth and not hard on palpation.

(*a*) *i.e.* the Patient is taken ill upon a Monday and the Rash appears upon the Tuesday.

(*b*) *i.e.,* the Patient is taken ill upon a Monday and the Rash appears upon the Wednesday.

(*c*) *i.e.,* the Patient is taken ill upon a Monday and the Rash appears upon the Thursday.

(*page 61*)

TYPHOID FEVER:—

The *rash* appears upon the fifth day after onset of the illness, but it is never easy to find.

It is confined to the abdomen and back.

It appears as successive crops of rose red spots, each crop quickly fading.

The foci are not hard on palpation.

GERMAN MEASLES:—

It resembles a mixture of mild editions of ordinary measles and scarlet fever.

ERYSIPELAS:—

Usually begins at the site of a wound or of an abrasion. There is an initial rigor, followed by vomiting, headache, and elevated temperature. Acute inflammation spreads over the skin surface, with a well defined raised edge at its spreading margin.

For special *treatment*, paint the affected area twice daily with Ichthyol 20% solution.

INFLUENZA:—

In a typical attack there is headache, prostration, aching pains in the calves of the legs and in the small of the back, and the temperature is elevated.

A rash is unusual.

DIPHTHERIA:—

At the onset the patient feels generally unwell, and has a "sore throat," with a little pain on swallowing. Within 24 hours there is a white film on the tonsils or the palate. The tonsil condition may be mistaken for follicular tonsillitis; in the latter, however, the white membrane is in patches representing the outside of the plug of each infected

110

follicle (*see* p. 50). A rash is uncommon.

(*page 62*)

The bacteriological report upon the "throat swab" will confirm or refute the diagnosis.

Diphtheritic anti-toxin is required for the *treatment*.

MUMPS:—

There is marked inflammatory swelling of the parotid gland, usually both, which makes swallowing, jaw opening, and neck movements painful.

There is no rash. It is very infectious.

WHOOPING COUGH:—

It usually begins as a cold in the head, which settles down as a peculiar paroxysmal cough or "whoop." The whoop is due to laboured inspiration, after the patient has emptied his lungs (as far as it is possible for him to do so) of air, after a succession of expiratory efforts.

There is no rash; it lasts for a long time, and it is very infectious.

ALCOHOLIC INTOXICATION:—

If an opinion is asked for as to whether a person is intoxicated from alcohol, satisfy yourself upon the following points:—

(1) Does his breath smell of alcohol?

(2) Is he in an excited condition?

(3) Does he talk sense or nonsense?

(4) Is his speech thick?

(5) Can he successfully pronounce the test words "Shibboleth" and "Biblical Criticism"?

(6) Does he stagger in walking?

(7) Can be stoop down and pick a pin up from the floor steadily?

N.B.—It is a wise thing to make a written note of your findings immediately after the examination, in case your evidence should be called for at a court of enquiry.

(*page 63*)

TREATMENT OF POISONING:—

The stomach may be emptied by washing it out, or by administering an emetic.

Useful ordinary emetics are:—(*a*) one tablespoonful of mustard powder mixed in a tumblerful of warm water; (*b*) two tablespoonfuls of common salt in a tumblerful of warm water.

(1) *Strong Alkalies, e.g.,* caustic soda:—

Give vinegar well diluted with water to neutralise the alkali.

Do not wash the stomach out.

Give quarter of a pint of olive oil in one pint of warm water, also give plenty of milk.

Keep the patient warm.

(2) *Alcoholic:*—

Either wash the stomach out, or give an emetic.

Give hot coffee.

Keep the patient warm.

(3) *Poisonous Gases:*—

Fresh air.

Artificial respiration.

Stimulants, *e.g.,* alcohol or strychnine.

Keep the patient warm.

Administer saline solution rectally or subcutaneously.

(page 64)

EXAMINATION OF A MAN FOUND UNCONSCIOUS:

If he is not dead—

(1) Smell his breath for any abnormal odour.

(2) Are his respirations faint or stertorous?

(3) Is it possible to rouse him (shout in his ear, and test the conjunctival reflex)?

(4) Hold his four limbs up separately; note if they fall inert when released, or if there is any rigidity.

(5) Are the pupils equal or unequal, and do they react to light?

(6) Are both knee jerks present; if so are they equal in activity?

(7) Feel the pulse; particularly note the rate, volume, and the rhythm.

(8) Is there any bleeding from the ears, nose, or mouth?

(9) Take the temperature.

(10) Test the urine (if any can be obtained) for albumen, sugar, renal casts, &c.

He may be suffering from—

Alcohol.

Post epileptic coma.

Apoplexy.

Compression of the brain, *e.g.*, due to a fractured skull.

Concussion of the brain.

Diabetes.

Opium.

Uraemia.

FITS:—

Incontinence of either urine or faeces during a "fit" is good evidence of an organic cause, and the most probable is epilepsy.

If there is never incontinence of urine or faeces during "fits," a diagnosis of functional nerve disturbance (hysteria) will probably be correct.

(page 65)

CONCUSSION OF THE BRAIN:—

A patient with concussion may be regarded as being near to death, and is worst at the time of the accident. From the time of the accident onwards he gradually recovers, *i.e.* if he is going to.

It presents the following features:—

The respirations are faint.

The patient can be roused, but with difficulty; the conjunctival reflex is usually present.

There is no paralysis of the limbs.

The pupils are equal, small in size, and they react to light. In the worst cases the pupils are equal, dilated, and do not react to light.

The knee jerks are present and equal in degree; in the worst cases these reflexes are absent.

The pulse is regular, small in volume, and quick.

The temperature is subnormal.

Actual recovery is nearly always preceded by vomiting; then he turns over on his side, flexes his thighs, pulls up the bed clothes about his shoulders, and wishes to sleep.

COMPRESSION OF THE BRAIN:—

This can result from anything which tends to reduce the available space in the cavity of the cranium; examples of this are — intra-cranial bleeding, a depressed fracture of the skull, intra-cranial abscess, &c.

Compression of the brain with unconsciousness presents the following features:—

The respirations are slow, noisy, and stertorous.

113

The patient cannot be roused, the conjunctival reflex is absent.
There may be paralysis of a limb or limbs.
The pupils are usually *un*equal in size, and do not react to light.

(*page 66*)

The knee jerks may be absent on one side or on both.
The pulse is regular, bounding, and slow.
The temperature is elevated, and more so on a paralysed side.
The urine and faeces are passed in bed.

SIGNS OF DEATH:—

Respiration ceases, use an ear or a mirror.
The circulation stops; use a stethescope, and feel for heart-beat or pulse.
The cornea loses its normal lustre.
The eyeball loses its elasticity.
The temperature falls.
The body becomes white or greyish-white in colour.
There is stiffening of the muscles, *i.e.*, rigor mortis.

Index to *The Clinical Notes*

(page 67)

	Page
Abdomen, inspection of	11
Abdomen, palpation of	12
Abdominal wall, rigidity of	12
Abscess, cardinal features of an	42
Acute abdominal diseases, list of some	5
Acute abdominal pain and opium	14
Acute abdominal pain and purgatives	14
Acute abdominal tuberculosis	5
Acute anaemia	29
Acute Bright's disease	55
Acute dilatation of the heart	24
Acute gastritis	18
Acute general peritonitis	17
Acute infectious fevers	32, 59 to 62
Acute iritis	43
Acute mastoiditis	52
Acute rheumatism	55
Alcoholic intoxication examination for	62
Analysis of abdominal symptoms and signs	8 to 13
Antisepsis and antiseptics	46
Appendicitis, acute	14, 15, 42
Asepsis	46
Back pain after an injury	52
Bandaging, dangers of tight	49
Bladder, inflammation of the	38
Bladder, stone in the	38
Bladder, tumour of the	39
Bleeding from gastric or duodenal ulcer	45
Bleeding, internal	29
Boils	50
Bone pain, worse at night	39
Boracic acid solution	47
Bright's disease, acute	55
Bronchitis	44
Burns	49
Calculus, renal	20
Carbolic acid solution	47
Carbuncle	50
Cartilage of knee joint, ruptured	40
Cellulitis of neck	49

(page 68)

	Page
Cerebro spinal meningitis	43
Chancroid	55
Chicken pox	59

	Page
Chronic inflammation, causes of	41
Clinical investigation of a case	6
Colic, intestinal	21, 57
Compression of the brain	65
Concussion of the brain	65
Conjunctivitis	52
Constipation	43
Consultation with surgeon	3
Cough with expectoration	44
Cough without expectoration	44
Cyanosis	24
Cystitis	38
Death, signs of	66
Diarrhoea	57
Diphtheria	61
Duodenal ulcer, ruptured	16
Dyspepsia, flatulent	56
Ear, chronic discharge from	52
Endocarditis	55
Epididymitis, acute	27
Epileptic fit	64
Epiphysitis, acute	41
Erysipelas	61
Fevers, acute infectious	32, 59 to 62
Fissure-in-ano	35
Fistula-in-ano	36
Fits	64
Flatulent dyspepsia	56
Flatus, inability to pass	19
Foreign body in eye	52
Fracture, examination and treatment of a	49
Fractured pelvis	30
Fractured ribs	31
Gastric crisis	28
Gastric ulcer, ruptured	16
Gastritis, acute	18
German measles	61
Gonorrhoea	54
Gonorrhoeal arthritis	40

(page 69)

	Page
Gonorrhoeal ophthalmia	53
Gonorrhoeal rheumatism	54

Haematemesis 45
Haemorrhoids 34, 35
Head, retraction of the 43
Headache 43
Heart apex, position of the 8
Heart dilatation, acute 24
Hernia 51
Hernia, strangulated 12, 43
Hernial sites, position of the 51
History of case, how to obtain 6

Inability to pass flatus 19
Infectious fevers, acute 32, 59 to 62
Inflammation 41
Influenza 61
Insomnia 56
Inspection of abdomen 11
Internal bleeding 29
Intestinal colic 21
Intestinal obstruction, acute 19
Intestinal rumblings 19
Iodine in the presence of mercury 47
Iritis, acute 43

Jaundice 45
Joint conditions 39
Joint, examination of a 39
Joints, positions for immobilisation of 40
Joint inflammation which is stationary 40
Joint inflammation which is transient 40

Kidney inflammation, acute 55

Lead poisoning 21, 57
List of acute abdominal diseases 5
Lord Lister 46
Lotions, and how to prepare them 46
Ludwig's Angina 49

Measles 60
Measles, German 61
Melaena 45
Mumps 62
Muscle wasting near joints 40

(page 70)

Page
Nervous patient 56

Obstruction, acute intestinal 19
Onset in an acute abdominal lesion 8
Opium, contra-indication for 14
Osteo-arthritis 40
Osteo-myelitis, acute 41
Otitis media 52

Pain in an acute abdominal lesion 9, 42
Pain in the back following injury 52

Pain and tenderness 42
Palpation of the abdomen 12
Pediculosis 57
Peristalsis, increased 19
Phlebitis 51
Physical signs of a tumour 33
Piles 34, 35
Pleurisy, acute 23
Pneumonia, acute 22
Poisoning, treatment of 63
Prostatic abscess causing acute retention 37
  of urine
Pulse rate 10, 33
Purgatives and acute abdominal pain 14
Pyelitis, acute 25

Questions for any rectal disease 34
Questions for any urinary disease 37

Rashes, varieties and examination of 58
Rectal carcinoma 36
Rectal diseases, questions relating to 34
Rectal polypus 36
Renal calculus 20
Respirations 11
Restlessness 29
Results of an inflammation 41
Retention of urine 37
Rheumatism, acute 55
Rigidity of the abdominal wall 12
Rigor 8
Routine for examination of a patient 6
Ruptured bladder 30
Ruptured semilunar cartilage of knee-joint 40
Ruptured gastric or duodenal ulcer 16
Ruptured viscus 14, 16, 30

(page 71)

Page
Saline solution 46
Scabies 57
Scarlet fever 60
Sciatica 56
Ship's painter, the 57
Shock 48
Skin diseases 58
Sleeplessness 56
Small-pox 60
Spirochaetae 55
Sterilisation of a wound 47
Sterilisation of hands 47
Sterilisation of surgical instruments 46
Stomach, dilated 43
Stone in the bladder 38
Stricture of the urethra 37, 39
Symptoms, how to elicit 6
Syphilis 54

116

Tabes Dorsalis 28
Temperature 10
Tender areas of the abdomen 12
Tender areas in diagnosis 42
Tongue appearances, analysis of some 11
Tonsillitis 50
Treatment of acute infectious fevers 59
Tumour of the bladder 39
Tumour, physical signs of a 33
Typhoid fever 61

Unconscious man, examination of 64
Uraemia 43

Urinary diseases, questions relating to 37
Urine 11
Urine, acute retention of 37

Varicocele 51
Varicose veins 51
Venereal disease, routine examination for 54
Venereal disease and blood infection 54
Vomiting 9, 43

Whitlow, varieties and treatment of 50
Whooping cough 62
Wounds, treatment of 47

APPENDIX A

APPROXIMATE NUMBERS OF SURGEON PROBATIONERS SERVING IN THE WAR.

1914	126
1915	176
1916	236
1917	200
1918	301
	1,039

APPENDIX B

SURGEON PROBATIONERS: THE YOUNG MEDICAL
STUDENTS WHO SERVED IN THE ROYAL NAVY
DURING THE FIRST GREAT WAR OF 1914-1918.

By

Dr R S Allison, VRD DSc MD FRCP DPM
Office of Archives, Royal Victoria
Hospital, Belfast.

Appendix to Journal of the Royal Naval
Medical Service. Vol.63 (1977) No. 1.

(page 2)

Name	1914 Date of Seniority	Appointed To
Eric Lander Caldwell Smith	April	HMS SOUDAN
Alfred Henry Price	June	HMS SOUDAN
Edmund Kean	July	HMS SOUDAN
Alfred G McColl	July	HMS DRINA
John Prescott Johnson	July	HMS ROHILLA
Howel Pennant Williams	July	HMS DRINA
William Tudor Evans	July	HMS ROHILLA
William Griffiths	July	HMS ROHILLA
William Griffiths	July	HMS DRINA
Noel A Scott	August	HMS ROHILLA
Charles Edward Kindersley	August	HMS ROHILLA
William Guy Emblett Allen	August	HMS ROHILLA
Robert Percival Langford-Jones	August	HMS ROHILLA
Philip Hudson	August	HMS PLASSY
Charles Humphry Gow	August	HMS PLASSY
Lionel Meredith Davies	August	HMS SOUDAN
Colin Roy Mackenzie	August	HMS SOUDAN
Herbert Guy Moser	August	HMS SOUDAN
Hugh John Dingle	August	HMS PLASSY
Keith Mason	August	HMS DRINA
William Felix Eberli	August	HMS REWA
Alan Osborne Courtis	August	HMS REWA
Bertram Baker Silcock	August	HMS REWA
Charles Harley Savory	August	HMS CHINA
Harold Williamson	August	HMS DRINA
Alfred Gregson Williams	August	HMS DRINA
Alfred William North	August	HMS DRINA
William Howard Pickup	August	HMS CHINA
Frederick Arthur Vere Denning	August	HMS REWA
Walter Herbert Butcher	August	HMS PLASSY
Frederick Harry Nicholas	August	HMS CHINA
H Cecil Craven Veitch	August	HMS CHINA
Walter Francis Raphael Castle	August	HMS REWA
Richard Wilfrid Fawcett	August	HMS PLASSY
Harold Boultbee Padwick	August	HMS REWA
Robert Ockleston Townend	August	HMS CHINA

Trevor Cecil Russell	August	HMS REWA
Ernest Cecil de Mallet Morgan	August	HMS PLASSY
Robert James Inman	August	HMS PLASSY
Noel Parry Price	August	HMS SOUDAN
Edward Victor Briscoe	August	HMS CHINA
John Gasperine	August	HMS PLASSY
Basil Haskins	August	HMS PLASSY
Henry Evers	August	HMS DRINA
Grahame Donald	August	HMS REWA
Eric P Hicks	August	HMS REWA
George F V Anson	August	HMS CHINA
George Sydney Strathers	August	
Theo Rosser Fred Kerby	August	HMS MINSTREL
Allan Gordon Bee	August	HMS NONSUCH
Edward Davenport Broster	September	HMS LYSANDER
Stanley E Y Elliott		
Stanley E Y Elliott	September	
James Maurice Harrison	September	HMS ERNEST

(page 3)

1914

Name	Date of Seniority	Appointed to
Harold G Stormer	October	
Geoffrey Francis Cobb	October	
Edward Arthur Holmes	October	
Roger H Clarke	October	HMS FIREDRAKE
H W L Molesworth	October	
A G Lennox-Browne	October	HMS MURRAY
John Adrian Dudley Skinner	October	TBD LEONIDAS
William B Heywood-Waddington	October	
Cecil N Ratcliffe	November	HMS ACORN
Arthur G Brett	November	HMS ACORN
Alfred F Wyatt	November	
Ernest A Hardy	November	HMS CAMPANULA
David B S Jones	November	HMS ANGLIA
E A Fiddian	November	HMS NEREID
Stewart R Johnston	November	HMS NYMPHE
Philip E F Frossard	November	HMS REDPOLE
Bertram H Pidock	November	HMS STAUNCH
Herbert W Eddison	November	HMS SANMAREZ
Gilbert Blurton	November	HMS COCKATRICE
Robert S Caldwell	November	HMS ORBITA
Thomas W Drummond	November	HMS HARDY
Alexander J Muirhead	November	HMS MIDGE
Ernest James Coombe	November	HMS SPARROWHAWK
Alexander Grey McKee	November	HMS UNITY
D Henry Ferris	November	HMS VICTOR
George Shuttleworth Barnett	November	HMS HONEYSUCKLE
Edward Wilson Drury	November	HMS LLEWELLYN
Theodotus J Sumner	November	HMS ARIEL
George Edward Mullins	November	HMS ORWELL
Edward Alexander Leak	November	HMS LIZARD
David Heard	November	HMS FOXGLOVE
Robert Thomas Stoney	November	TBD HIND
Thomas James Lane	November	HMS NEPEAN

William Philip Elford	November	HMS RAVEN II
Cecil Broadhurst	December	HMS ACHATES
James Alexander Stirling DSC	December	HMS METEOR
Thomas Cleave Wakefield	December	HMS OWL
John Thomas Wylie	December	HMS LIVELY
Geoffrey Burman Lowe	December	HMS LOCUST
Angus McAlpine Scott	December	HMS SPRIGHTLY
Lewis Livingstone Fotheringham	December	HMS FERRET
Alfred William Cocking	December	SPECIAL SERVICE
Duncan William MacKay	December	HMS MILNE
George Osmond Grant	December	HMS MAENAD
John Dutton Byrd	December	HMS VICTORIAN
William Oliver Lodge	December	HMS GHURKA
Canning Suffern	December	HMS GRIFFIN
David Leishmann Baxter	December	HMS OUSE
John Arnold Molony Alcock	December	HMS ITCHEN
Charles McDonald	December	HMS AFRIDE
Godfrey Anthony Paris	December	HMS AMAZON
Norman Keane Henderson	December	HMS COSSACK
Christopher Thomas Helsham DSC	December	HMS CRUSADER
William Wallace King Brown	December	HMS MAORI
William O'Gorman Donoghue	December	HMS CAMELLIA
Peter Gerald Stevenson Davis	December	HMS CHEERFUL
Walter Aslatt Turner	December	HMS MORRIS
Noel Arthur Hamilton Barlow	December	HMS MURRAY

(page 4)

1914

Name	Date of Seniority	Appointed to
David Shields Prentice	December	HMS STAG
Paul Herbert Shelley Smith	December	HMS VIGILANT
William James McBain Allen	December	HMS MALLARD
George Murray Shaw Lindsay	December	HMS COLUMBELLE
Duncan Reid Macnicol Nicol	December	HMS ANDES
Reginald Joseph Patchett	December	HMS ACACIA
George Albert Clark	December	HMS ANEMONE
John Frederick Haynes	December	HMS DIGBY
Dennis Athelstone Knight	December	HMS PATIO
Joseph Evelyn Phillips	December	HMS PATUCA
Francis Reginald Law	December	HMS MOTAGUS
Thomas Lavellin Puxley Harries	December	HMS CHANGUINOLA
James Fairbrother	December	HMS OROTAVA
George Pearson	December	HMS GOLDFINCH
Norman Sinclair Hewitt	December	HMS HILAR
Harry Stephenson Lucraft	December	HMS HILDEBRAND

1915

William E Boyd	January	HMS COLUMBINE
William Langwill Hunter	January	HMS GOSHAWK
James Shaw	January	HMS CHANGAINOL
Douglas Stuart Stevenson	January	HMS FORESTER
Ernest Bracewell Kelley	January	HMS NERISSA
Neil MacLeod	January	HMS SANDFLY
Donald Stewart	January	HMS MIRANDA

Henry Godfrey Fitz-Maurice	January	HMS SHELDRAKE
Ralph Coyte	January	
James Ewart Purves	February	HMS MYRTLE
Alexander Taylor Woodward	February	HMS LEONIDAS
Harold Edward Andrews	February	HMS MENTOR
Philip Sydney Marshall	February	HMS LUCIFER
Percy Gilbert Horsburgh	February	HMS MORRIS
John MacRae Sandilands Nichol	March	
Clifford Riley Watson	March	HMS MYNGS
Norman Jennings	March	HMS WAVENEY
Alger Roy Oram	March	HMS TEST
John Harold Ewen	March	HMS HORNET
James Biggam Douglas Galbraith	March	HMS ROTHER
Andrew Oliver Ross	March	HMS STOUR
Lindsay Gordon Allan	March	HMS AVON
Frank Macgregor Ferguson	March	HMS ALBATROSS
Donald William Warren	March	HMS PEVERILL
Frederick George Edward Hill	March	HMS ATTACK
Percy Ward	March	HMS BADGER
Harold Knight-Denham	March	HMS LARK
Edward Oliver Morrison	March	HMS GARLAND
John Grant Gilruth	April	HMS METEOR
James Witherspoon Duncan	April	HMS EBRO
Francis Roy Cripps	April	HMS MANSFIELD
Joseph Clinton Collins	April	HMS ORCOMA

(page 5)

1915

Name	Date of Seniority	Appointed to
Kenneth Langthorne Stanley Ward	April	HMS ALCANTARA
James P Johnston	April	HMS ALCANTARA
George William Marshall Findlay	April	HMS THORN
John Mirtle Redpath	April	HMS LOUIS
George Lambert Cutts	April	HMS LAFOREY
Joseph Paton Fleming	April	HMS MILNE
Samuel Murdock Riddick	April	HMS LIZARD
Herbert John Leviseur	May	
John Joseph Carrol	May	HMS KALE
George Ernest Spero	May	HMS NESS
John Clifford Brown	May	HMS LAUREL
Montague Horace Jupe	May	HMS MEDEA
Reuben Woodland Payne	June	
John Stephen McGrath	June	HMS CHRISTOPHER
John Bruce Watson Telford	June	HMS MOORSAM
Herbert William Hall	June	HMS MELAMPUS
John James Keatley	June	HMS OROPESA
J Ebenezer MacIntyre	June	HMS ARDENT
George Edmonson Birkett	June	HMS LOYAL
Bernard Stanley Collings	June	HMS HARDY
Francis Hessey-Anderson	June	HMS LEGION
Philip Barlow	June	HMS PARAGON
Hewitt Jones	June	HMS LIBERTY
Henry Tomlinson	June	HMS VIXEN
Robert Philip Crawford	June	HMS HIND
John Adam Lewis	June	HMS ALYSSUM
Robert Sydney Steele Smith	July	HMS TEUTONIC

Leonard Heatley Woods	July	HMS CEDRIC
James Murray Macpherson	July	HMS BUTTERCUP
Thomas Scott	July	HMS BRISK
Harold Gordon	July	HMS CARNATION
John William Scharff	July	HMS MONS
John Herbart Blackburn	July	HMS VIRGINIAN
Alexander Joe	July	HMS NESTOR
Raymond O'Connell Redmond	July	HMS CLAN MACNAUGHTON
David McEachran	July	HMS LINNET
Currie Carruthers Craig	July	HMS LILY
Alexander MacRae	July	HMS CAMELEON
Vincent Gatt	July	HMS EGMONT
Barryhill Moore	July	HMS CETO
R Walker	July	HMS SHARK
Barclay Barrowman	July	HMS ALMANZORA
Ronald Douglas MacKenzie	July	HMS MINSTREL
Murdock Davidson	July	HMS ASPHODEL
William Andrew Byrn	August	HMS LAWFORD
Duncan Brian Macgregor	August	HMS PETEREL
Alexander MacPherson	August	HMS NIGELLA
Donald John Morrison	August	HMS LEONIDAS
Harold Larcom Mooney	August	HMS LANDRAIL
Francis Malcolm Timothy Fintan	August	HMS NYMPHE
Douglas Ian Otto Macaulay	August	HMS REDPOLE
John Gibson	September	HMS MORESBY
Peter Alexander MacKay	September	HMS MARTIN
Kenneth Frazer Darrell Waters	September	HMS PORPOISE

(*page 6*)

1915

Name	Date of Seniority	Appointed to
John Milton Davey	September	HMS MOON
Robert McCall Burnie	September	HMS NARCISSUS
Ian Ross Macphail	September	HMS NEREID
William Malcolm Macphail	September	HMS BADGER
William Brodie Moore	September	HMS MANSFIELD
Bernard de Medina Greenstreet	September	HMS HYDRA
James Davidson	September	HMS UNITY
John David Arthur	September	HMS TARA
Hubert Llewellyn Pridham	September	HMS MENTOR
John Robinson	September	HMS MAGIC
Stanley Cyril Mitchell	September	HMS EXPRESS
John Kenneth Crawford Liddell	September	HMS LENNOX
Richard Hartley Rose-Innes	October	HMS GOSHAWK
Geoffrey Norman Wardle	October	HMS ORCOMA
Walter Ernest Heath	October	HMS LIBERTY
John Learmont	October	HMS VIENNA
Thomas Stewart Stirling	October	HMS MATCHLESS
Philip Clermont Livingstone	October	HMS GLOUCESTERSHIRE
Daniel May Watson	October	HMS PHOENIX
John Donald	October	HMS MIDGE
David Hardie Williamson	October	HMS GARLAND
David James Tosh Oswald	October	HMS NOMAD
Henry Morrison	October	HMS PATUCA
John Hislop	October	HMS RUBY
William Edgar	October	HMS MANNERS

Name	Date	HMS
Cecil Edward Ede Herington	October	HMS VERONICA
Japil Harold Leopold Shapiro	October	HMS ASTER
Howard Sidney Plowman	October	HMS COMET
Daniel Donovan	October	HMS CONTEST
Humphrey Josh Hollis	November	HMS GODETIA
Donald Maclean	November	HMS LOOKOUT
John William Peden	November	HMS HILARY
Harold Bernard Alexander	November	HMS ALARM
Donald Eadie Brown	November	HMS AMAZON
Howard Leister Douglas	November	HMS MELAMPUS
Robert Pollock	November	HMS RIFLEMAN
Desmond Villiers Townshend	November	HMS MICHAEL
Charles Barclay Reekie	November	HMS MOLDARIA
John Nicol	November	HMS MORREL
Thomas Norman D'Arcy	November	HMS ONSLOW
Normal Nelson Kirkup	November	HMS MARMION
Henry Walter Breese	November	HMS AMBUSCADE
Christopher Hugh Macklin	November	HMS OROTAVA
James Struthers Clark	November	HMS SWIFT
Fred Wilson	November	HMS LAUREL
Donald Hugh Cameron	November	HMS ACASTA
Douglas George Patrick Bell DSC	November	HMS SPITFIRE
Alexander Ritchie	November	HMS OBDURATE
Richard Erskine Batson	November	HMS DAHLIA
George Buchanan	November	HMS MORNING STAR
G S Freeman	November	HMS LASSOO
Richard Ryther Stancer Bowker	December	HMS PELICAN
Alexander Thomas Harrison	December	HMS PRIMROSE

(page 7)

1915

Name	Date of Seniority	Appointed to
Charles Ainger Kirton	December	HMS ACHESON
Thomas Anderson	December	HMS LAVENDER
Eric George Theodore Holden	December	HMS JESSAMINE
Alexander Coutts Fowler DSC	December	HMS IRIS
Duncan MacCallum Blair	December	HMS GLADIOLUS
Donald Rankin	December	HMS NORBOROUGH
Hugh William Young Taylor	December	HMS SAGITTA
John Hamilton Crawford	December	HMS NEREID
William Michael	December	HMS SNOWDROP
Archibald Campbell Lindsay	December	HMS ROSEMARY
David Tweedy Watt	December	HMS ZINNIA
Henry Poston	December	HMS LINNET
Watt McRovie	December	HMS COCKATRICE
Ivan Curror Christie Barclay	December	HMS MARY ROSE
Alexander Riach Forbes	December	HMS DAFFODIL
James Charles Sleigh	December	HMS LABURNUM
Thomas Anderson	December	HMS LAVENDER
James Henry Kerr	December	HMS EDINBURGH CASTLE
William Leslie Berry	December	HMS LOCHINVAR
Frank Robertson Mitchell	December	HMS ARCHER
Edward Jocelyn Bilcliffe	December	HMS MONITOR
Thomas Francis Broderick	December	HMS LARKSPUR
Thomas Gilliland Campbell	December	HMS LUCIFER
Sylvester Joseph Healy	December	

George Dixon Fisher McFadden	December	HMS LAVEROCK
John Skinner MA	December	HMS MANTUA
Hugh Paul	December	HMS CHRISTOPHER
Duncan Brown	December	HMS MENACE
James Morrison Ritchie MA	December	HMS SPARROWHAWK
Graham Arthur Osborne White	December	HMS CAMPANIA
L G P St J Story	December	HMS OPAL
Alexander Shanks Bisset	December	HMS GENTIAN
John Fraser Kerr	December	HMS MIRANDA
Alex McCheyne Mackintosh	December	HMS OTWAY
Henry Hamilton Bailey	December	HMS RUBY
N Spencer Naire	December	HMS LUFICER

1916

Bryce F Niblock	January	HMS NOBLE
Rex O'Connor	January	HMS DAPHNE
Samuel Andrew Gailey	January	HMS OBEDIENT
Robert Leslie Stewart	January	HMS MUNSTER
Frederick Hugh Smith	January	HMS ACHATES
Wilfred Francis Attwater	January	HMS NEGRO
William Shearer	February	HMS CITY OF LONDON
John Hale	February	HMS LOYAL
Henry Thomas Cubbon	February	HMS LANDRAIL
James Alexander Lumsden-Cook	February	HMS MASTIFF
William Edward Mandall Wardill	February	HMS FORESTER
Percy Banbury	February	HMS TIGRESS
Frederick V Jacques	February	HMS ONSLAUGHT
Arthur Clare Halliwell	February	HMS MIMOSA
Charles Cottrill Ralph Downing	February	

(page 8)

1916

Name	Date of Seniority	Appointed to
Arthur Howard Henry	February	HMS MEDEA
Frederick Harold Richards	February	HMS STAG
Robert Douglas Lockhart	February	
John Martin Higginton	February	HMS LARCHER
Alexander Dickson McHaffie	February	HMS GERANIUM
James Joseph Nolan	February	HMS AVENGER
Edmund Stuart Orme	February	HMS WALLFLOWER
Thomas Lucas Hillier	February	HMS MAGNOLIA
John Paul Spencer Walker	February	HMS MINOS
Frank Neon Reynolds	February	HMS OAK
Victor Millington Synge	February	HMS PETEREL
Frank Sutcliffe Horrocks	February	
Robert Weaver	February	HMS AVOCA
Lionel Charles Goument	February	HMS MUSKETEER
Frederick Paul Nigel Parsons	February	HMS RAPID
John Sinclair Westwater	February	HMS CAMELEON
Tyrrell George Evans	February	
Charles Girdlestone Terrell	February	HMS LAVEROCK
Arthur Alston Ward	February	
Charles Eric Cobb	February	HMS PARTRIDGE
Richard Norman Gibson	February	HMS BEAVER

Thomas Caryle	February	HMS DEFENDER
William George Thompson	February	HMS JACKAL
Carl Knight Cullen	February	HMS MISCHIEF
Arthur Welsby Kirkham	February	HMS ROWENA
Robert Lawrence Walker	February	HMS ACASTA
William Stanley Sykes	February	HMS SABRINA
Alfred Ernest Gallaher	February	
Alfred Innis Cox	February	HMS MANLY
Percival Sommerville Walker	February	HMS NARWHAL
Roy John Farmer	February	HMS LEGION
Alister Roderick Matheson	February	
Cedric Kennedy Scales	March	
Geoffrey Wyatt Pratt	March	HMS MARGUERITA
Gordon Millar	March	
Gerald Hartas Fitzgerald	March	HMS ATTENTIVE
John Myles Birkerton	March	
Cyril James Thomas	March	
Robert Macnair	March	HMS DRUID
Lewis Henry Bartram	March	
Edward Phillimore Brockman	March	
William Malcolm McAlister	March	
Andrew Francis Briglmen	March	HMS BASILISK
Arthur Wellwood Mackie	March	HMS MOTOGNA
Thomas Morley Cunnington	March	
Kenneth McFadyean	March	HMS WISTARIA
Edward Douglas Thomas Roberts	March	HMS SANDFLY
Harpur Vernon Edwards	March	
John Francis Howell	March	HMS CROCUS
John Saunders Lewis Roberts	March	HMS DELPHINIUM
Andrew Macpherson	March	
Claude Young	March	
William Adamson Gray	March	
James Reid	March	HMS LILAC
Harold George Taylor	March	

(page 9)

Name	1916 Date of Seniority	Appointed to
Jos. Marshall McCaldin Wright	March	HMS PATRICIAN
John Churchill Blake	March	HMS MYOSOTIS
Edgar Gordon Adams	March	HMS ANEMONE
James Stewart Durward	March	HMS CYCLAMEN
Aubrey Claud Forster Barrow	March	HMS LIZARD
Norman Trenholme Williamson	March	HMS STAG
Algernon Sanders Green	March	
Kenneth Tratman King Wallington	April	HMS SNAPDRAGON
Stanley Roy Tattersail	April	HMS LOBELIA
Alexander Crofton Sleigh	April	HMS MARGUERITE
Ernest Kenneth Macdonald	April	HMS ARIEL
John Douglas Magor Cardel	April	HMS HOLLYHOCK
Norman James Macdonald	April	HMS CELANDINE
Robert Ebenezer Kerr	April	HMS BERBERIS
Eric J Edward	April	
George Humphry Ward	April	HMS MANNERS
James Leslie Wilson	April	HMS OSIRIS
William Howel-Evans	April	HMS CORNFLOWER

126

Thomas Clyde McKenzie	April	HMS MAMELUKE
Francis Normal Victor Dyer	April	HMS BUTTERCUP
John Ryan	April	HMS VALERIAN
Eric Vere Corry	April	HMS LAPWING
William Gordon Robson	April	HMS HIMALAYA
Josiah William Chalmers Fairweather	April	HMS HYDRANGEA
Edward Roeley Pierce	April	
Alexander Ledingham Strachan	April	HMS GENISTA
Chadwick	April	
Kenneth George Harman Brown	April	HMS ORACLE
Kenneth Macilennan Purves	April	HMS KALE
John Vickerman Mainprize	April	HMS HARDY
Arthur Herbert John Smart	April	HMS PATRIOT
Oswald Stuart Thompson	April	HMS MALLARD
Dudley Eyre Ross	April	HMS LINNET
Harold Scott Trefry	April	HMS NEREID
Ronald McDonald Cairns	April	HMS ACHERON
John James Rouse Binnie	April	HMS OSSORY
Duncan Fergusson Yuille	April	HMS SABLE
Donald Alexander Cunningham	April	SPECIAL SERVICE
John Alexander Ross	April	HMS NOBLE
Alexander McCallum Millar	April	SPECIAL SERVICE
Trevor Alexander Howard Smith	April	HMS ORPHEUS
Charles Clement Beney	April	HMS BLUEBELL
Henry Thomson	May	HMS MAENAD
John Kennedy Murray	May	HMS MEDWAY
Frank Gray	May	HMS VICTOR
George Eldred Rae	May	HMS CHANGUINOLA
Norman Burnet Gadsby	May	HMS OWL
David Livingstone Macrae Tod	May	HMS PEONY
Walter Tyrrell Benson	May	
Oliver Gray	May	HMS COCKATRICE
James Newlyn Gale	May	HMS MASTIFF
St George Bernard Delisle Gray	May	HMS STAUNCH
John Allan	May	HMS HILARY

(*page 10*)

	1916	
	Date of	Appointed
Name	Seniority	to
John William Stewart Blacklock	May	HMS PEREGRINE
David Coupar Lamond	May	HMS TERMAGANT
Maurice Kirkpatrick Jardine	May	HMS TRIDENT
Gilbert Paterson	May	HMS HIND
Gerald William Thomas Hunter Fleming	May	
Edward Leslie Ewan	May	HMS UNITY
Francis Wharton Lemarchand	May	
Andrew Buchanan Macdonald	May	HMS ATTACK
Edward Matheson Fraser	May	HMS CONTEST
Ernest Algernon Sparks	May	HMS LIGHTFOOT
Douglas McClean	May	HMS MORRIS
Douglas Crawford Clark	May	HMS PORPOISE
John Lupton Taylor	May	HMS PENN
Archibald Donald Brown	May	HMS PHOENIX
William George Robertson	May	HMS METEOR
James Gibson Campbell	May	HMS WOLVERINE
Farquhar McVean	May	HMS ASPHODEL

Reginald Arthur Hickley	May	HMS PENTSTEMON
Samuel Burnside Borthwick	May	HMS LILY
Alexander Gavan Morison	June	HMS EDINBURGH CASTLE
Pierce Lloyd-Williams	June	HMS NERISSA
James Stewart	June	HMS WALLFLOWER
Roland Ephraim Rawson Sanderson	June	HMS PORTIA
Robert Frederick Boltman	June	HMS VERONICA
John Kohler Steel	June	HMS GABRIEL
James Paterson	June	HMS ALYSSUM
Wilfred Mark Anthony	June	SPECIAL SERVICE
Robert McGarrol	June	HMS RUBY
Edwin John Gostwick Sargent	June	HMS CAMELLIA
Murdock Brown	June	HMS OBSERVER
Peter MacMurray	June	HMS MENACE
Arthur Hugh Shelswell	June	HMS ACHATES
James Richard Hughes	June	HMS GARLAND
John Stuart Lewis	June	
Ellis Pigott	June	HMS MINOS
Sidney Hill Waddy	June	HMS RESTLESS
Bernard Woolcott Thompson	July	
Gwilym Evan Morgan	July	HMS MILLBROOK
Geoffrey William Theopold	July	HMS CHRISTOPHER
Arthur Gordon Ord	July	HMS FORESTER
Sydney Carver Woodhouse	July	HMS OBDURATE
Frank Young	July	HMS SUNFLOWER
John Stephen Moore	July	HMS ROCKET
William A Whitehouse Parkes	July	HMS RIFLEMAN
Charles John Slim	July	HMS MUNSTER
Joseph Harold Sheldon	July	HMS WISTARIA
Donald Fraser McGregor	July	SPECIAL SERVICE
Reginald Edward Hopton	July	HMS MYNGE
William S Adams	July	HMS MORESBY
Charles Courtney Bennett	July	HMS FOXGLOVE
Alfred Pilkington Bertwistle	July	HMS LLWELLYN
Charles Reginald Cade	July	HMS BEAVER
William Devereux Forrest	July	HMS MEDINA
Ernest Lowe	July	HMS HILDEBRAND
Hugh Pennefather Warren	July	HMS CAMELEON
Herbert Edward Williams	July	HMS MIDGE

(page 11)

	1916	
Name	Date of Seniority	Appointed to
Hugh Donovan	July	HMS PLUCKY
Harvey Nicol	August	HMS NONSUCH
Hugh Graeme Topping	August	HMS NEPEAN
Andrew Weir Davison	August	HMS READY
Harold James Phillips	August	HMS PATUCA
James Sinclair Quin	August	HMS RAIDER
James Baird	August	HMS LYSANDER
P Canney Arnold	August	HMS PRINCE
Gerald Joseph Moore	August	HMS HORNET
Ralph Byron Gibson	August	HMS LAFOREY
Cecil Emrys McQuade	August	HMS ARLANZA
Thomas Madill	August	HMS LARK
Evelyn Cecil Whitehall Cooke	August	HMS PATIA

Gilbert Rashleigh Hull	August	HMS PETARD
Horace Sharman Le Marquand	August	HMS ROSEMARY
James Caddies	August	
Charles Nathaniel Armstrong	September	RNB CHATHAM
Charles Ernest Scott	October	
Henry Alexander Ross	October	HMS LOOKOUT
John Hetherington	October	
Gordon Patrick Walker	October	
Gifford Campion Thornton	October	
Ernest Edwin Carter	October	
Robert Fletcher	October	
George Alexander Sinclair	October	
Joseph Patrick McMillan	October	HMS PARTHIAN
Francis McDonald	October	
William Leslie Belfour	October	HMS PHOENIX
Thomas Victor Carey	October	HMS NORTHESK
P F Pratt	October	HMS TARTAR
John Logan Lamond	October	
John Paton Hope	October	HMS SURPRISE
Frank Carlton Jones	October	HMS ORESTES
William John Payne	October	HMS DELPHINIUM
John Lawrence Dooley	October	HMS CROCUS
Archibald Joseph Cronin	October	HMS MELAMPUS
William Swirles Allardyce	October	HMS NEGRO
Robert Adam Forsyth	October	HMS ORIANA
Richard Wood Power	October	HMS NORSEMAN
Francis Denis Gillespie	October	HMS OPHELIA
John Henry Brenell Crosbie	October	HMS OAK
Bernard Wilson Roffey	October	HMS OCTAVIA
David Reid	October	HMS ROMOLO
Charles Fergus McLean	October	HMS ORIOLE
Elliott Fraser Brown	October	HMS MUSKETEER
Alister Campbell	October	HMS GOSHAWK
Victor George Walker	October	HMS PORPOISE
Kevin Robert Chapple	October	HMS SANDFLY
Arthur Mather Horsey	October	HMS MILNE
Frederick Wm. Robertson	November	HMS MEDEA
Joseph Black	November	
Gerald Fitzmaurice Keatings	November	
Ronald Henry Ottywell Betham Robinson	December	HMS OBERON
Edwin Ronald Ormerod	December	HMS NORMAN
Colin Macphail Forbes	December	HMS MIGNONETTE

(page 12)

	1917	
	Date of	Appointed
Name	Seniority	to
William Edward Mason	January	HMS LABURNUM
Arthur Thomas Hawley	January	HMS DAHLIA
Donald Arthur Cadman	January	HMS LIVEROCK
Cecil Arthur Horder	January	HMS REDOUBT
Osmond Hayman Brown	January	HMS LANCE
Thomas James	January	HMS LLEWELLYN
Edward Louis Adenorff	February	HMS PHOEBE
Robert Paulin Wanless	February	HMS STURGEON
William James McClintock	February	HMS HARDY
Ian Robert Spark	March	HMS ORCADIA

Lawrence Paul Garrod	March	HMS MOORSON
William Burleigh Parr	March	HMS VIENNA
Eugene Arthur Pearson	March	
George Hurrell	March	HMS LENNOX
Albert Ernest Blackley	March	
Albert Christian Lornie	March	HMS PEREGRINE
Louis Mosses	March	HMS CARNATION
Cecil Carron Brown	March	HMS OPPORTUNE
Douglas Rainsford Learoyd	March	
Urban Joseph Gareau	March	
Neil Robertson Beattie	March	HMS NIMROD
George Henry Weeber	March	
Alan Wordsworth Fawcett	April	
Alexander Hayward Harkins	April	
Arthur Walford Taylor	April	
Nicholas Dunscombe Dunscombe	April	
Ian MacLaren Thompson	April	HMS STRONGBOW
Arthur Markson	April	
Charles Scott Dickson	April	
William Beattie Dickson	April	
Robert Carr Hall	April	
Frederick Alexander Logan	April	
Alexander Lynn McKay	April	HMS UNDINE
William Gaynor Powell	April	
Wilfred Parsons Warner	April	HMS FORRESTER
John Franklin Docherty	April	HMS MATCHELESS
Robson Christie Brown	April	HMS MONS
John Binnie Taylor	April	HMS MASTIFF
Agnus Macdonald	April	HMS NICATOR
Roderick Montague Macpherson	April	HMS NARWHAL
Henry Arthur Aidan Pargoter	April	HMS MANLY
Clinto Edgar Manning	April	
Frederic James Stevenson	April	HMS LEONIDAS
Edwin Roland Sarra	April	HMS IRIS
George Anthony Goolden	April	HMS MATCHLESS
Alexander Lennox McAdam	April	HMS SHELDRAKE
Richard Alex Dudley Jefferson Bernhardt	April	
Walter de Mouilpied Scriver	May	SPECIAL SERVICE
Crawford Law Wilson	May	
Kenneth James Herbert Davies	May	HMS SARACEN
George Geoffrey Newman	May	
Arthur Sheard	May	HMS NONSUCH
James Alexander Law London	May	HMS TETRARCH

(*page 13*)

	1917	
Name	Date of Seniority	Appointed to
Geoffrey McKay Gibbon	May	HMS WALLINGTON
Charles Glen	May	HMS SCEPTRE
George Jamieson	May	HMS TYRANT
Charles Wilbur Harris	May	HMS REDGAUNTLET
William Allan Defoe	May	HMS AMBUSCADE
Gordon Campbell Cameron	May	HMS ACHERON
Wilbur James Cryderman	May	HMS WISTARIA
Robert Young Paton	May	HMS THRUSTER
Alan McKenzie	May	

Henry Charles Victor Toy	May	HMS TERMAGANT
John Arthur Pilkington Shaw	May	HMS SATYR
Reginald Neville Kirk	May	HMS SARPENDON
Roydhu Ronald Wilson MacLaren	May	HMS NARCISSUS
Sidney Gilbert Harrison	May	HMS PANSY
Charles Raymond Thornton	May	HMS TEAZEL
Samuel Hawkridge Matheson	May	HMS CAMELIA
Harry W Quinn	May	HMS WALLINGTON
William E Johnston	May	HMS CYNTHIA
Robert E Joyce	May	HMS FAULKNER
Gordon L Bell	May	HMS FAME
Winfield H Miller	May	HMS FERRETT
Harold I Palmer	May	HMS URCHIN
Thomas B Feick	May	HMS PHOEBE
Harold S Little	May	HMS GRASSHOPPER
George Edward Strahan DSO	May	HMS STORK
William Tighe	June	HMS CETO
Grant Elmslie	June	
Peter Crawford Rankin	June	HMS VANQUISHER
David Gordon Robertson	June	HMS WAKEFUL
Donald Woods Winnicott	June	HMS LUCIFER
John Irvine Milne	June	HMS TAVER
Donald Mackenzie	June	HMS PLUCKY
Alexander Jephcott BA	June	SPECIAL SERVICE
John Gilchrist Coltart	June	HMS FERRET
William Beaumont	June	HMS LAUREL
Hugh Allan Morton	July	HMS WALLINGTON
Barry Thomas Roper-Hall	July	HMS SKILFUL
Douglas Marshall Lindsay	July	HMS OSIRIS
Hugh Leslie Mather	July	HMS SYBILLE
Donald Victor Latham	July	HMS HONEYSUCKLE
Cedric Holmes	July	HMS HONEYSUCKLE
Cedric Holmes	July	HMS CORNFLOWER
Aubrey Dudley Gill	July	HMS LENNOX
William Randolph McNie	July	HMS TORRENT
Thomas Swinhoe Severs	July	HMS MOUNSEY
Campbell Shaw	July	HMS KESTREL
Richard Victor Dowse	July	SPECIAL SERVICE
Thomas Francis John Hopwood	July	HMS TRUCULENT
Peter Wilson	July	IIMS WIZARD
John Trevor Burrell	July	HMS BUTTERCUP
John Beaumont Gregor	July	HMS MEDEA
Colin Charles Bradsworth	July	HMS VALERIAN
Patrick Joseph Healy	July	HMS MARNE
John Edmund Basham	July	HMS MARTIAL
James Dunlop Whiteford	July	HMS LOBELIA

(page 14)

Name	1917 Date of Seniority	Appointed to
James Macdonald	July	SPECIAL SERVICE
Arthur Samuel Pearson	July	HMS SABLE
Arthur Harrison Hall	July	SPECIAL SERVICE
David John Whitton	July	SPECIAL SERVICE

Ronald Cunliffe Shaw	July	HMS TRIDENT
Archibald Rae	July	SPECIAL SERVICE
James Macfarlane	July	SPECIAL SERVICE
Wesley Cope Holdsworth	July	HMS BEGONIA
George McCoull	July	HMS SWIFT
James Innes Coventry	July	SPECIAL SERVICE
Frederick Cecil Wray Capps	July	HMS VORTIGERA
Archibald Glen Duncan	August	SPECIAL SERVICE
Alan Benjamin Stewart	August	HMS ROCKET
Eric Shaw Longton	August	HMS VENDETTA
Robert Menzies Galloway	August	SPECIAL SERVICE
Horatio D Low	August	
James Reid David	August	
Gerrard Burnett	August	P.63
George Percival Monk	August	HMS MELPHONEME
Eric Richard Murray	August	HMS POPPY
George Tudhope	August	HMS CLEMATIS
Harold Randall Griffith	August	HMS LAPWING
James Reid	August	HMS CROCUS
Thomas Hobson Kirk	August	
Robert Cran McLennan	August	HMS DISCOVERER
Jos. Craig McNaught	August	HMS SUNFLOWER
Archibald Gordon Smith	August	HMS TAURUS
Sydney Win. Timpson Lee	August	HMS ROSEMARY
Alexander Edwin Reid	August	HMS MISCHIEF
Arthur Joseph de Lys O'Connor	August	HMS LYSANDER
Douglas Reginald Macdonald	August	HMS ONSLOW
Herbert Leyland Sackett	August	SPECIAL SERVICE
Maurice Danks Cadman	August	HMS RIVAL
Robert Leslie Dodds	August	HMS MAMELUKE
Thomas John Chapman	August	
Eric Cresswell Dagger	August	HMS RESTLESS
William Elliott Collinson	August	HMS VENTUROUS
William Smith Cochar	August	
Lloyd Egerton Verity	September	HMS MINION
Edwin Rayner Jagger	September	HMS OBDURATE
Harry Vernon Phelon	September	HMS NERCUS
Edwin Norman Duncan Reffer	September	HMS TERMAGENT
James Douglas Kinsman	September	HMS NIZAM
Alexander Lothian Brough	September	HMS HOPE
Peter Alexander Faichney(POW)	September	HMS PARTRIDGE
Horace Reese John Thomas	September	HMS SYLPH
Robert Williamson	September	HMS OFFA
John James Norman Daniels	September	HMS VANCE
Arthur Quinton Wells	September	HMS ULYSEES
George Francis Abercrombie	September	SPECIAL SERVICE
John Innes Moir	September	HMS MYRTLE
Charles Joiner	September	HMS MANDATE
David Bruce Wilson	September	HMS ALFRIDA

(page 15)

1917

Name	Date of Seniority	Appointed to
John Charles Groscort Reed	September	SPECIAL SERVICE
Harry Ray Bulmer	September	HMS PETUNIA

Robert Henry Jos. Malholl Corbet	September	HMS RAIDER
Henry Norman Whitham	September	HMS TRISTRAM
Albert William Darnley Magee	September	HMS CELANDINE
William Gordon McCormack	September	HMS ALARM
Charles Gibson Auld	October	HMS CAMELEON
Frank Whitely	October	HMS MILLBROOK
Henry James Horne	October	HMS SPRINGBOK
Alan Wilson Hart	October	HMS SYRINGA
Roland George Anthony	October	HMS RIFLEMAN
Frederick Herman Molliere	October	P.43
James Samuel Edward Manley	October	HMS LABURNUM
Reginald Clifford Williams	October	HMS SCOURGE
Albert James Constance	October	HMS ORPHEUS
George Garlach Graham	October	
Vincent Murray McAdam Watson	October	HMS PYLADES
James Oswald Lindsay	October	HMS OCTAVIA
French Senior Vaughan	October	HMS CYCLAMEN
Leslie James Timings	October	HMS HELIOTROPE
Thomas Whelan Panter	October	HMS ZINNIA
Arthur John Gardham	October	HMS TORRID
Peter Hutchinson	October	HMS TIGRESS
William Wilfred Dow	November	HMS VEGA
Lancelot Stewart Planche	November	HMS MARVEL
William Milroy Kennedy	November	HMS LAUREL
Ronald Gillan Cloustan	November	HMS BLUEBELL
Stanley Ackroyd	November	P.65
Hugh Archibald Wallace	November	HMS LURCHER
Andrew Morton Robertson	November	HMS SORCERESS
Lennox Matthew Johnston	November	HMS TRENCHANT
William Newton Walker	November	HMS TARTAR
Bernard Bowman	November	HMS REDOUBT
James Leather	November	HMS MEPOMONE
John Ezra Dunlop Miller	November	HMS OAK
Robert William Locke	November	HMS TALISMAN
John Henry Struthers	November	HMS MYSTIC
Reginald Pleasance	December	HMS TEMPEST
William Howroyd Smorfitt	December	HMS VIMIERA
William Livingstone Kennedy	December	

1918

John Grant	January	HMS LOCHINVAR
William Robert Paton Templeton	January	HMS FURY
William Lofley Tullis	January	HMS THRUSTER
George William Hollings	January	HMS SHARK
Edgar Sunderland Clayton	January	HMS WINDSOR
Wilfred Harvey Marston	January	SPECIAL SERVICE
Cedric Gordon Payton	January	
William Sinclair Moir	January	HMS VIVACIOUS

(page 16)

	1918	
	Date of	Appointed
Name	Seniority	to
	January	
George Gilbert Buchanan	January	
Gerald Frederick Staveley Parker	January	HMS DEFENDER
James Yates	January	HMS JACKAL

133

Eric John Llewellyn Jones-Evans	January	
Reginald Walter Roberts Watson	January	HMS PEYTON
David Slight	January	HMS VERULUM
Alfred Edward Beckwith	January	HMS ORIOLE
Charles C Elliott	February	HMS HORNETT
Charles Frederick Edmunds	February	HMS SKILFUL
Horace Collingbourne	February	HMS VENETIA
Griffith Wynn Owen	February	HMS TIRADE
John Roland Hetherington	February	HMS LIGHTFOOT
Horace Simkin Savage	February	HMS MILNE
Walfred George Mathieson	February	HMS REDPOLE
Arthur Bearblock	February	HMS ARCHER
Ogilvie Maxwell Duthie	February	HMS FLYING FOX
Gerald Cecil Wooton Curson	February	HMS LYCHNIS
Raymond Eustace Ford	February	HMS NIGELLA
George Roebuck Woodhead	February	HMS ACORN
Harold Edmund Emmett	February	HMS SHELDRAKE
John Eskdale Fishburn	February	HMS ASPHODEL
Frederick Lawrence Smith	February	
William Gilbert Desmond Harold Urwick	February	
Reginald Anderton	February	
Frederick Richard Hall	March	
Frank Moore Larkins	March	
Bertie Moorwood Tonkin	March	HMS HYDRA
Frederick Roper	March	
Christopher Wesley Narbeth	March	
John Victor Sparks	March	
Charles John de Vere Shortt BA	March	HMS MARTIAL
William George T Kirap Robinson	March	HMS VICEROY
William Geraghty	March	
Hugh Patrick Fay	March	
Daniel Joseph O'Meara	March	
James Aird Morton	March	
Noel Sydney Bailey Vintner	March	
John Andrew Mackay Ross	March	
Robert Handley Greaves	March	
William Mark Brown	March	
Hugh Reid	March	
William Aric Hallamore Banks	March	HMS SARPEDON
Philip Lawrence Richardson	March	
Edward Emile Delisle Gray	March	HMS MARTIN
Idwal Glynne Williams	March	
William Hedley Summerskill	March	
Leslie Ralph Augustus Wells	March	
Douglas C Bastow	March	HMS SYRINGA
Howard D McCart	March	HMS BRISK
Geoffrey Edward Woolcombe Felce	March	
Beresford T Richards	March	HMS ZUBIAN
Edward Savage	March	HMS SNOWDROP
John Patrick Tynan Mills	March	HMS SPIREA
Leslie Middlemiss Jennings	March	

(page 17)

1918

Name	Date of Seniority	Appointed to
Francis Robert Oliver BA	March	

Name	Date	Ship
George Spofforth Need	March	HMS RAPID
Harold Holtby	March	
Edwin Spencer Etheridge	March	
Beriah	March	
Philippe Cauacoud	March	
Frederick Cyril Cozens	March	HMS SNAPDRAGON
Austin Furniss	March	
Donald Hunter	March	
Robert Shaw Wayland	March	
Victor George Massie	March	
Edric Frank Wilson	March	
Harold Edwin Thomas	March	
Alexander Herbert Bean	March	HMS MYNGS
Eli Wilson Ewart	March	HMS VERONICA
Stanley H Sievenpiper	March	HMS RADSTOCK
William John Gibson	March	HMS MUSKETEER
Owen Fitzpatrick	April	HMS SHARPSHOOTER
Walter Breakell	April	
Charles James Cecil Earl	April	HMS LLEWELLYN
Lucas Piecters	April	HMS ACASTA
Norman Leslie Capener	April	
Henry Christopher Powell	April	HMS SEPOY
Thomas Bernard Hodgson	April	HMS AMAZON
Sydney George Haycraft Glasson	April	
Philip Cornelius du Toit	April	
Michael W B Bulman	April	
Reginald Walter Patrick Hosford	April	HMS SEYMOUR
David Summerville	April	HMS SCIMITAR
William Wilson	April	HMS HOLLYHOCK
Thomas Stewart Sargent	April	
Wilfred Walter Payne	April	
James Duff Stewart	April	
Edward Alexander Wilson	April	HMS JONQUIL
Robert Pedlow	April	HMS MEDEA
John Herbert Duke	April	HMS VENDETTA
Alec Hanson	April	
Johan Fredrik Wicht	April	
Alexander Gardner Aitken	April	HMS GARLAND
Robert Stanley Brunton	April	HMS OBERON
Walter Ralph Gill Hearnden	April	HMS MANSFIELD
George Milne Gray	April	HMS VEGA
James Arthur Kerr	April	HMS GOSHAWK
Leo Norton Knight O'Neill	April	HMS BEAVER
James Callaghan Souter	April	HMS FORESTER
David Owen Williams	April	HMS PLUCKY
Thomas Morgan Jones	April	HMS PEREGRINE
Alexander Lee McGregor	April	HMS PLOWER
Robert Gordon McIntyre	April	
George Leslie Meachim	April	HMS PATRIOT
William Christopher Wardle	April	HMS DUCHESS OF DEVONSHIRE
James Chronnell	April	HMS MOHAWK

(page 18)

	1918	
	Date of	Appointed
Name	Seniority	to
John Alexander Douglas	April	HMS HIND

135

Name	Date of Seniority	Appointed to
Alex Louis George Thompson	April	HMS NORSEMAN
William Logan Grassick MA	April	HMS MINION
Frederick W Haskett	April	HMS MISCHIEF
Herbert William Southgate	April	HMS PEONY
George William Cheater	April	HMS HAREBELL
William Davis	April	HMS LENNOX
Frederick Ferdinand Petersen	April	
George Robert Falcon	April	HMA RELENTLESS
John F V Chester	April	HMS MARGUERITE
Walter M Pamphelon	April	HMS MELPOMENE
Reginald G Ratz	April	HMS TIGRESS
John H McLeod	April	HMS TRIBUNE
Frederick J Nickle	April	HMS STORK
John D Gear	April	HMS MALAMPUS
Stanley Arnold Holling	April	HMS VALERIAN
George R Jones	April	HMS OFFA
Ivan W James	April	HMS NORMAN
Norman H Mitchell	April	HMS CORNFLOWER
John A Graham	April	HMS FIREDRAKE
Donald H Hubbs	April	HMS POLYANTHUS
Charles P Fitzpatrick	April	HMS OBSERVER
John Hammond Palmer	April	HMS LILAC
John Kendall	April	HMS TUBEROSE
Cyril Mayberry Probert	April	
Athelstan Woodman	April	HMS MINUS
Ralph Hodgson	April	HMS HEROIC
Allan Cameron Newman	April	HMS SWEETBRIAR
John Stanley Symond	April	HMS SCOTSMAN
William Guthrie Niblock	April	HMS WELLINGTON
William Joy Ward	April	HMS ITHURIEL
Emrys Jones	April	HMS VANOC
Thomas Latham	April	HMS VIVIAN
Norman Stewart Craig	April	HMS TRISTRAM
Leo Unsworth	April	HMS ULYSSES
James Robert Hylton Pasqual	April	HMS VIKING
Kenneth Leon	April	HMS WALPOLE
Charles John Lewis	April	HMS WATHERHEN
Adam Paterson	April	HMS WALLINGTON
Wilfred Thistlewaite	April	HMS DRUID
Donald Cook Marshall	April	HMS WADDINGTON
George Phil Driver	April	HMS BRYONY
Charles Haddon Wilson	April	HMS ARDPATRICK
William Craig Galt	April	HMS CLANTHUS
Philip Dilworth Abbott	April	HMS MONBRETIA
Richard Laurence Flint (serving with RAF)	April	
Albert Boswell Nutt (serving with RAF)	April	
William Stanley Russell Thomas	May	HMS BUTTERCUP
Robert Sturgeon Chapman	May	HMS LILY
George Richard Harold Cooper	May	HMS MICHAEL
Ian Stewart Thomson	May	HMS SENATOR
Evan Thomas Lloyd	May	HMS AFRIDI
Davis Evan Bedford	May	HMS TELEMACHUS
William Caithness	May	HMS OPPORTUNE

(page 19)

1918		
Name	Date of Seniority	Appointed to
George Alix Dempsey	May	HMS NONPARIEL

136

Samuel Whately Davidson	May	HMS MYSTIC
Jacobus Malan Bosman	May	HMS ORESTES
Philip George Bainbridge	May	HMS MORRIS
William James Chapman	May	HMS OXFORD
Thomas Arnoldus du Toit	May	HMS PHOEBE
Frank Edward Edwards	May	HMS LOCHINVAR
George William Murray	May	HMS CHRISTOPHER
Arthur Ingham	May	HMS SABLE
Percival Fildes	May	HMS ACHATES
George Archibald Barter	May	HMS MANNERS
William Goodacre Roberts	May	HMS WINDFLOWER
William Ewart Neale	May	HMS RADIANT
James Worthington	May	HMS SKATE
Arthur Arnold Osman	May	
Harold Grover Armstrong	May	HMS VIOLA
Arthur Carmen Gordon	May	HMS PRIMROSE
Smith Lancelot Everett Danby	May	HMS GARDENIA
William Douglas Swan	May	HMS BERBERIS
Sydney Charles Skipper	May	HMS SIRDAR
Ross Moore Jewell	May	HMS MARREL
Bernard Charles Sullivan	May	HMS SAXIFRAGE
Henry Norman Jaffe	May	HMS MILNE
John Gerald Dunlea	May	HMS VOYAGER
Guy Burford Tarring	May	HMS SCOUT
Colin Campbell Mackinnon	May	HMS CRUSADER
James Hamilton Doggart	May	HMS SIKH
William Ewan Douglas Hodgson	May	HMS PARTRIDGE II
Frank Hiam	May	HMS VERULAM
James Joseph Doyle	June	HMS SIR BEVIS
Tom Robert Ernest Hillier	June	HMS OCTAVIA
Harold Orville Macnamara	June	HMS MORESBY
Graham Albery Jordan	June	HMS VANQUISHER
Harry Gordon Clark	June	HMS WOLFHOUND
George Todd Zumstein	June	HMS LIZARD
Lawrence Edward McCaffrey	June	HMS CHRYSANTHEMUM
Harold Roy Moon	June	HMS LEPANTO
John Stanley Ferguson	June	SPECIAL SERVICE
Edward Arnold Grey Branch	June	HMS NEPEAN
James Wallace Hepburn Smith	June	HMS GERANIUM
Arthur Ezra Riddell	June	IIMS MAGNOLIA
Robert Murray Pendrigh	June	HMS LIBERTY
George Edward Trimble	June	HMS MALLOW
William Bolt	June	HMS SARNIA
Harold Austin Whitcomb	June	HMS SABRINA
Alfred Henry G Down	June	HMS CROCUS
William Yuill Jamieson	June	HMS NEREUS
George Francis Watson	June	HMS HYDRANGEA
Harold Glenn Stevenson	June	HMS PELICAN
Walter Francis Charteris	June	HMS NICATOR
Frederick Harold Wilson	June	
Gordon Robert Hain	June	HMS WHITLEY
Egerton Simon Moete Shunk	June	HMS MUNSTER
Malcolm Donald MacQueen	June	

Name	1918 Date of Seniority	Appointed to
Arthur Gordon Armstrong	June	HMS HEATHER
Milburn Watts Kemp	June	HMS SWIFT
William Edward Woods	June	HMS SILENT
Richard Norman Clarke Richardson	June	HMS LANDRAIL
William Clarence Atwell	June	HMS LINNET
Samuel James Stewart	June	HMS NARWHAL
Ernest George O'Shea	June	HMS TARPON
Harold Aloysius Lomax	June	HMS TEMPEST
James Browne Wiley	June	HMS OBEDIENT
Stephen Douglas Sturton BA	June	HMS PALADIN
Wilfred Shaw	June	HMS SWALLOW
Charles Cecil Howard Chavasse	June	HMS FURY
Bernard Hart	June	HMS OSIRIS
Walter Edmund Beck	June	HMS OBDURATE
Charles Davey Crawford	July	HMS LANCE
Walter Lascelles	July	
John Russell Craig	July	HMS NORTHESK
John Robert Dallow	July	HMS RESTLESS
James Christie Anderson	July	HMS MEDINA
Richard Sydney Allison	July	HMS ACORN
Christopher Howard Andrewes	July	HMS MARIGOLD
Egerson Charles Grey	July	HMS NEREID
Albert Stanley Bradlow	July	HMS CORCOPSIS
James Robertson Wills	July	HMS MARJORAM
Graham Lee Chambers	July	HMS LYRA
John Charles Richard Edwards	July	HMS DIANTHUS
John Oswald Green	July	HMS ROCK SAND
Francis Charles Maddon	July	HMS ANEMONE
Daniel Cornelius	July	HMS PARTHIAN
Michael Joseph Heney	July	HMS ICY
Francis Edward Jones	July	HMS TILBURY
Laurence John Walters	July	HMS SPARROWHAWK
Russell Whicher Stephens	July	HMS NARCISSUS
David Meikle	July	HMS KNIGHT TEMPLE
William James Alexander Russell	July	HMS MASTIFF
Arthur Hugh McCulloch Eaton	July	HMS HONEYSUCKLE
John Scott Lyle	July	HMS ALARM
Joseph Eugene Deane	July	
Vivian Stephen Fournier	July	HMS CLEMATIS
Edmund Burke Nagle	July	HMS DONOVAN
Dudley Thomas Fournier	July	HMS AZALEA
John Shanks	July	HMS PETARD
Howard Lascombe Raynor	July	HMS TORCH
William Allen Murphy	July	HMS HORNET
Lambert Charles Rogers	July	HMS SUNFLOWER
Greenville Windsor St Clari Ramsey	July	HMS ACACIA
George Septimus Moran	July	HMS JESSAMINE
Percy Bellwood Farrar	July	HMS TANCRED
William Alexander Back	July	HMS RIFLEMAN
David Charles Williams	July	HMS TRENCHANT
John Macfarlane Cray	July	HMS VEGA
Thomas Edward Crozier	July	HMS LOBELIA
Charles Ronald Christian	August	HMS CYCLAMEN
Thomas Gerald Warham	August	HMS SPEEDY
Patrick Paul Daly Connolly	August	HMS SYLPH

(page 21)

Name	1918 Date of Seniority	Appointed to
John Douglas Thompson	August	HMS MARKSMAN
William Harden Smith	August	HMS REDOUBT
Thomas J Davidson	August	HMS TEAZEL
William McCartan	August	HMS PENTSTEMON
Robert Thompson	August	HMS CICERO
Patrick Grant Cumming	August	HMS TRINIDAD
Thomas Arthur Crane Strevens	August	HMS ORMONDE
Leonard Gray Morrison	August	HMS LAPWING
James Rannie	August	HMS SEFTON
Charles William de Villiers-Pritchard	August	HMS TRIDENT
Alexander Ian Corr	August	HMS TORRID
Alistair Campbell Dewar	August	HMS AURICULA
William Aiken Brown	August	HMS VORTIGAN
Frederick Martin Allen	August	HMS MIRANDA
Samuel Avid McCleery Thompson	August	
James Nixon Morris	August	HMS WESSEX
Robert Johnston	August	HMS CAMPANULA
Conrad Vincent Patrick	August	HMS LURCHER
Stanley Allwright Gunter	August	HMS ZINNIA
E Hugh Weatherall	August	HMS KEMPENFELT
Andrew Gibb	August	
Thomas Symington Storey	August	HMS SILVIO
Francis Maybury Hilliard	August	

Index to *The Surgeon Probationers*

Abercrombie, G.F., V.R.D. Surg. Prob. to H.M.S. *Onslaught, Lightfoot, Velox, Warwick* and *Trident*. Served in H.M.S. *Warwick* under Admiral Keys for operations against Zeebrugge and Ostend, 35

Acheson, Samuel, Surg. Prob. to H.M.S. *Laverock*, rejoined as Surg. Lieut. in 1918, 19

Action between British destroyers and German light cruisers, 34

Adriatic barrage, 48

Allen, F.M.B., Surg. Prob. to H.M.S. *Miranda*, 17, 22

Allison, R.S., Surg. Prob. to H.M.S. *Acorn*, 26

American troops arriving at Southampton, 42

Bain, D., 1st Lieut. R.N., 48
— Capt. of H.M.S. *Norfolk* during Second World War and took part in the destruction of the *Bismark*, 57

Balfour, W., Surg. Prob. to H.M.S. *Phoenix*, killed in action, 37

Barclay, I.C., Surg. Prob. to H.M.S. *Mary Rose*, killed in action, 35

Bearblock, Mr., Surg. Prob. to H.M.S. *Goshawk*, 49

Beaver, H.M.S., 51

Beck, W.A., Surg. Prob. to H.M.S. *Rifleman*, 27

Beck, W.E., Surg. Prob. to H.M.S. *Obdurate*, 27

Belfast Medical School, contribution of in surgeon probationers, 15, 27

Bell, D.G.P., Surg. Prob. to H.M.S. *Spitfire*
— Awarded D.S.C. for 'great attention to the wounded', 30

— Account of experiences at Jutland, 30-33
— Subsequent career, 33

Blenheim, H.M.S., 50

Bolt, W., Surg. Prob. to H.M.S. *Sarnia*, killed when ship mined, 41-42

Brisk, H.M.S., 54

British Medical Association, 6, 7

Brittania, H.M.S., 52

Browne, W.A., Surg. Prob. to H.M.S. *Versatile*, 27

Cabin, availability in destroyers limited, 12

Caithness, W., Surg. Prob. to H.M.S. *Opportune*, 22

Carlill, Hildred, Staff Surgeon, R.N., 39

Caroline, H.M.S. and Ulster Division, R.N.V.R. & R.N.R., 15
— Hall, Robin, Surg. Prob. and P.M.O., Ulster Division, 15

Christian, C.R., Surg. Prob. to H.M.S. *Cyclamen*, 27

Christmas Day in Sevastapol, 56

Commissioning of Surgeon Probationers, 8, 9

Como, Lake, 52

Crozier, T.H., Surg. Prob. to H.M.S. *Lobelia*, 26, 46

Critchley, Lieut., V.C., 54

Dardanelles, 56
— rage at sailor for bringing back to ship human skull, 56

Dodds, R.L., Surg. Prob. to H.M.S. *Mameluke*, 22

Dreadnoughts, 48

Duke, J.H., Surg. Prob. to H.M.S. *Vendetta*, 27

Dunn, J.H., Surg. Prob. to H.M.S. Triton, 25

Durazzo, attack on, by combined fleet, 51

Eaton, A.H.McC., Surg. Prob. to H.M.S. Honeysuckle, 26, 53, 57

Faichney, P.A., Surg. Prob. to H.M.S. Partridge taken prisoner-of-war, 35

Fanshawe, Captain D., 53

Fowler, A.D., Surg. Prob. under Admiral Campbell's 'Q' ships, awarded D.S.C. for conspicuous bravery, 34

Gaussen, J.F.H., Surg. Prob. and re-entered navy on graduation, attaining rank of Surg. Capt., R.N., 22

Giles, Sub. Lieut., R.N.V.R., 50

Gillespie, Leonard, Physician to Lord Nelson, 2

Goeben, German battle cruiser, 54

Grand Duke & Duchess Alexander, rescued by H.M.S. Acorn, 56

Hall, H.E., Surg. Commander, R.N.V.R., 19
— Surg. Lieut. H.M.S. Concord, 19
— P.M.O. Naval Base, Londonderry, and later II.M.S. Furious, 19

Hall, Robin, Surg. Prob. and P.M.O., Ulster Division, R.N.V.R., 15

Haslar, Royal Naval Hospital, 11, 38, 39, 39, 41
— Canadian students at, 38
— dinner in medical mess at, 39
— treatment of an hysterical patient, 39
— H.M.S. Victory in 1918, 40
— Anaesthetics at, 40
— officers and necessity to carry gloves, cane and not to smoke in the street, 41

Helsham, C.T., Surg. Prob. to H.M.S. Broke
— Awarded D.S.C. for gallantry under fire, 33

Influenza Epidemic, 50

Ismid, Gulf of, 53

Johnston, R., Surg. Prob. to H.M.S. Campanula, 27

Jules Michelet, Armoured French cruiser, 54

Jutland, Battle of, 28-30

Killoch, Mr., Warrant Engineer, 47

Lascelles, W., Surg. Prob. (1918), 27

Lee, S.W.T., Surg. Prob. to H.M.S. Rosemary, 22

Lyle, J.S., Surg. Prob. to H.M.S. Alarm, 26

Lytle, W.J., Surg. Prob., 19

MacKenzie, J.N. Bowen, Commander R.N., 47

Malta, Arrival at on Armistice Day, 52

May, Surgeon General Sir Arthur, 5, 6

Medical Stores, 12

Moffitt, F.W., Surg. Prob. to H.M.S. Gurkha

McCartan, W., Surg. Prob. to H.M.S. Pentstemon, 26, 43, 43, 44

McFadden, G.D.F., Surg. Prob. to H.M.S. Archer, 19
— his extraordinary experiences when washed overboard, 21

Novorrisk, 56

Paul, Hugh, Surg. Prob. to H.M.S. Shark, 19

Pedlow, R., Surg. Prob. to H.M.S. Medea, 23

Perry, Mr., Warrant Gunner, R.N., 47

Plassy, H.M. Hospital Ship, 13, 16

Poston, H., Surg. Prob. to H.M.S. Linnet, 20

Prize Money: Good effect on medical recruitment, 2

Queen's University of Belfast, Services Club, 15

Rats in ships, view of sailors, 25
Regulations governing surgeon probationers, 8, 9, 10
Rohilla, H.M. Hospital Ship, 11
Royal Marines, Landing party in support of, 55
Royal Naval Volunteer Reserve, 12
Royal Navy:
—State of preparedness of war, v
— Potential role of aeroplane, torpedo and submarines, 1
— Shortage of naval medical officers in 1914, 2
— Comparison with R.A.M.C., 5
— Address of Surgeon General Sir Arthur May, 5, 6
— British Medical Association and shortage of medical officers, 6, 7
Royal Army Medical Corps, 4

Schools, Irish Medical, contribution of, 15
Smith, E.L.C., Heads Navy List of Surgeon Probationers, 11
Soudan, H.M. Hospital Ship, 11
Stirling, A., Surg. Prob. to H.M.S. *Meteor*
— Awarded D.S.C. for exceptional bravery at Dogger Bank Action, 33
Storey, P.G., Surg. Prob. to H.M.S. *Opel*, drowned when ship lost off Orkneys, 19
Strahan, G.E., Surg. Prob. to H.M.S. *Stork*
Stork
— Awarded D.S.C., 34
Surgeon's Mates, the predecessors of Surgeon Probationers, 3, 2
Surgeon Probationers:
— Commissioning of, 8, 9, 10
— System of rotation, 12
— Regulations governing, 8, 9, 10

Sykes, S., 'A land lover of the deepest dye'. Article on his experiences as surgeon probationer, 24-25
Synge, V.M., Surg. Prob. H.M.S. *Petrel*, 16

Temerere, H.M.S., 54, 55
Tozer, Leading Seaman, coxswain to H.M.S. *Acorn*, 48
Troop train, experiences in journey overland to Toronto, 43-45

Victory, H.M.S. in 1918, 40

Waddy, S.H., Article on experiences as surgeon probationer, 25
Westwater, J.S., Surg. Prob. to H.M.S. *Swift*, 33
— Awarded D.S.C. for gallantry under fire, 34
Weymouth, H.M.S., Light cruiser torpedoed at Durazzo, 52
Wiley, J.B., Surg. Prob. to H.M.S. *Obedient*, 20
Wilkinson, Sub. Lieut., R.N., 47
Willan, R.J., Staff Surgeon, R.N.V.R., 13
— In H.M.H.S. *Plassy* at Scapa Flow, 13
— Member of Council R.C.S.(Eng.), 13
— Medical Advisor to Prince Albert, 13
— Hon. Surg. to King George V., 13
— Surgeon Rear Admiral, 13
— Author of 'Clinical Notes for Surgeon Probationers', 14
— Prof. of Surgery, Durham University, 13
— Death 1955, 14
Willis, Sub. Lieut., R.N., 53